COMPREHENSION
NINJA
FOR AGES 7–8:
FICTION & POETRY

ANDREW JENNINGS
WITH ADAM BUSHNELL

BLOOMSBURY EDUCATION

LONDON   OXFORD   NEW YORK   NEW DELHI   SYDNEY

BLOOMSBURY EDUCATION
Bloomsbury Publishing Plc
50 Bedford Square, London, WC1 3DP, UK
29 Earlsfort Terrace, Dublin 2, Ireland

BLOOMSBURY, BLOOMSBURY EDUCATION and the Diana logo are trademarks of
Bloomsbury Publishing Plc

First published in Great Britain, 2021 by Bloomsbury Publishing Plc

A catalogue record for this book is available from the British Library

ISBN: PB: 978-1-4729-8985-7; ePDF: 9-781-4729-9122-5

2 4 6 8 10 9 7 5 3 1

Text design by Marcus Duck Design

Printed and bound in the UK by Ashford Colour Press

To find out more about our authors and books visit www.bloomsbury.com and sign up for
our newsletters

CONTENTS

OTHER NINJA RESOURCES

FOR TEACHERS

VOCABULARY NINJA

A practical guide containing strategies and photocopiable activities to help transform pupils into vocabulary ninjas. Featuring theory and teaching approaches, as well as key topic vocabulary, etymology and phrases, this book will bring the primary curriculum to life.

COMPREHENSION NINJA NON-FICTION

A set of six books for ages 5–11 that provide strategies and photocopiable resources to teach comprehension. Each book presents 24 high-quality non-fiction texts and photocopiable activities with strong links to the National Curriculum.

FOR CHILDREN

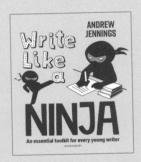

NINJA WORKBOOKS

Vocabulary and comprehension workbooks to support learning at home. Each workbook contains bespoke non-fiction texts and hundreds of questions that are linked to the National Curriculum. Perfect for developing literacy skills and boosting children's confidence in literacy and reading comprehension.

WRITE LIKE A NINJA

A pocket-sized book full of all the grammar, vocabulary and sentence structures that children need in order to improve and develop their writing skills. Fully aligned to the Key Stage 2 National Curriculum, this book is designed to be used independently by pupils both in the classroom and at home.

FURTHER RESOURCES FOR SCHOOLS, TEACHERS AND CHILDREN ONLINE

Head to www.vocabularyninja.co.uk and follow @VocabularyNinja on Twitter for more teaching and learning resources to support the teaching of vocabulary, reading, writing and the wider primary school curriculum.

INTRODUCTION

THE COMPREHENSION NINJA: FICTION & POETRY SERIES

The Comprehension Ninja: Fiction & Poetry series has been designed to be an essential resource for teaching reading comprehension skills and building pupil confidence. The books focus on information retrieval, using core comprehension skills that underpin the reading domains set out by the National Curriculum.

Each of the six books in the series contains 24 awesome fiction and poetry texts, followed by comprehension activities. The texts have been curated to feature a range of authors, genres and text types from the world of children's literature and poetry.

Quite often, comprehension activities can bombard pupils with a range of question types that they have not yet had time to master – meaning they quickly encounter questions that they find extremely challenging. This series places the emphasis on teachers being able to teach and model each skill, while pupils develop their understanding of each question type individually.

PROGRESSION AND DEVELOPMENT OF SKILLS

The books in the Comprehension Ninja: Fiction & Poetry series grow in difficulty via the complexity and length of the texts. The vocabulary in the book for ages 7–8 is more challenging than the vocabulary in the book for ages 5–6, for example. The length of the reading texts falls in line with statutory assessments at Year 2 and Year 6, growing in increments each year, thus increasing the demands on pupils to accurately retrieve information from larger and more complex texts.

Approximate text length* in the Comprehension Ninja: Fiction & Poetry series:

Ages 5-6:   100-150 words
Ages 6-7:   200-250 words
Ages 7-8:   300-450 words
Ages 8-9:   500-600 words
Ages 9-10: 650-700 words
Ages 10-11: 700-800 words

*Within each age range, the poetry texts can vary from the word count ranges shown above. In these instances, the reduced word count is complemented by more complex vocabulary and sentence structures.

HOW TO USE THIS BOOK

This book contains 24 fiction and poetry texts for you to use in your classroom. Part 1 includes 12 texts that have eight subsequent pages of questions built around different comprehension skills. These texts and questions have been developed so that you can specifically target and teach each individual skill, and then have a plethora

of questions for pupils to work on. In maths, you wouldn't jump from division one day into 3D shapes the next. The same must apply to reading – we should teach each skill and give pupils the opportunity to practise and master the skills before we move on. You now have in your hands 12 texts with associated questions to teach each skill – that's a minimum of 96 lessons from Part 1 of the book.

Part 2 includes texts 13 to 24 and these look more like traditional tests. Each text has a corresponding set of questions. Each set of questions requires pupils to use the comprehension skills mastered in Part 1. You could choose to use these texts formatively across the year to inform which skills require further attention, but here lies a fantastic opportunity for pupils to apply their new skills to each question type independently and with confidence.

It is important to note that this resource hasn't been designed to be a testing tool but rather a teaching and learning tool. A tool whereby teachers support pupils to access texts and to master core comprehension skills. However, because of the nature of testing in schools, it is important that children see and experience test-type texts and questions – as they will from Part 2.

This is a versatile resource: it's up to you how it is used. As pupils grow in confidence and skill level, they will relish completing these activities.

PRE-READING AND KEY INFORMATION TO IDENTIFY IN THE TEXT

Before they answer questions, teach pupils to pre-read a text and identify key information using a pencil or a highlighter.

Here are some examples of the key information pupils could be encouraged to look out for when they read fiction or poetry.

Who or which? Characters, people, animals, events, and so on.

When? Time periods, including times of the day, days, months, years, and so on.

Where? Locations or changes in location.

What or how? Actions that characters perform, linked to verb phrases.

Vocabulary: Key vocabulary that is relevant to understanding and words that pupils are unfamiliar with.

Dialogue: Conversations between characters.

We want to train pupils to underline or highlight pieces of key information as they read through the text. A good guideline is to underline or highlight three-to-six pieces per paragraph. Key information should be single words, or small groups of words, not full sentences. Model this skill to pupils and discuss why you have underlined certain information. As well as physically marking the text, model your thought processes too, showing pupils how you make mental notes about locations, characters, actions, and so on.

KEYWORDS IN THE QUESTION

Once pupils have read the text and underlined key information, they can begin to answer questions about it. We now need to teach pupils to spot keywords or key phrases in a question. These are words or phrases that signpost where to look in the text to find the answer. Take a look at this question:

Why was the dinosaur near to tears?

Pupils should be taught to underline 'near to tears'. They would then need to skim through the text to find the section where the phrase 'near to tears' can be found, then scan that section to find the exact phrase. After this, pupils should be taught to read the sentences or lines before and after the one that contains the key phrase. This will help them find the answer. Pupils might understand that the word 'dinosaur' is not necessarily a helpful keyword, as it is likely to be repeated many times in the text.

Pupils might not understand what the keywords in the question mean. However, they can still answer the question by finding the keyword or key phrase and reading around it.

THE QUESTION TYPES

✏️ FILL IN THE GAP

Pupils are given sentences with missing words. They will need to locate the sentences in the text and identify the missing words. Refer pupils back to their pre-reading and marking of the text, which should increase their retrieval speed.

> **NINJA NOTES**
>
> Practise this skill by giving pupils a page of their reading book and the same page with multiple words blanked out. Can they fill in the blanks? Prompt pupils to spot keywords in the rest of the sentence in order to locate the full sentences in the original text.

❓ FIVE Ws AND HOW

These are classic reading comprehension question stems: what, where, who, which, when and how. All of these require pupils to retrieve information from the text to demonstrate their understanding.

> **NINJA NOTES**
>
> Constantly refer back to the pre-reading process and model this skill to pupils, demonstrating how, as a reader, you are constantly identifying the five Ws as you read. Say your thoughts as you read the text aloud, demonstrating how you make mental notes of the question words as you read. Model to pupils how you can begin to predict what the questions are likely to be.

◎ MULTIPLE CHOICE

These questions require pupils to choose an answer from a selection of four possible answers. Prompt pupils to locate the required information by spotting keywords in the question and locating them in the text, then reading around this information to find the correct answer.

> **NINJA NOTES**
>
> Teach pupils to discount illogical answers using what they already know from their pre-read of the text. Also ensure that pupils don't answer questions using their own prior knowledge. Prompt pupils to 'prove it' by finding the exact information in the text.

👆 TRUE OR FALSE

Pupils are given a statement and asked if it is true or false. Younger year groups will begin to learn this skill by answering yes or no, before progressing to true or false.

> **NINJA NOTES**
>
> Ensure pupils are not guessing. Train pupils to spot the keywords in the questions and locate this information in the text. By reading around this information and pre-marking the text, pupils will be able to discover whether the statements are true or false.

🖊️ SUMMARISE

Summary questions require pupils to understand the main idea or main piece of action in a section of text. For some questions, pupils will have to select the correct summary statement from multiple options, while for other questions they will need to write a short summary.

> **NINJA NOTES**
>
> Refer to the concept of summarising as 'What is the main idea of this section of text?'. Try to find opportunities for pupils to summarise information during reading sessions and in other subjects such as history or science.

🖌️ DRAW AND LABEL

Draw and label requires pupils to draw an image based on the information they have read and then to add their own labels.

> **NINJA NOTES**
>
> Increase the difficulty of labelling by asking pupils to label more complex images. Alternatively, use draw and label as part of your literacy lessons.

123 SEQUENCING

These questions require pupils to sequence information in the order it occurs in the text, from first to last.

FIND AND COPY

These questions require pupils to identify a word when provided with a contextual description rather than a contextless definition. Pupils will need to use keywords to locate the correct area of the text and then find and copy the correct word. For older pupils, questions may direct pupils to a certain part of the text at the beginning of the question, for example, *Look at the verse beginning 'Maggie just froze…'.*

CIRCLE A WORD

This skill requires pupils to locate words based on an explicit definition of the word. Pupils may be required to circle words from a single sentence or from a paragraph of the text.

READING AND EXPLOITING FICTION AND POETRY TEXTS WITH YOUR PUPILS

The Comprehension Ninja: Fiction & Poetry series offers so much more than information retrieval. The series offers an unrivalled and unique collection of texts and poetry from a range of poets and authors.

So, how else could you use this treasure trove of texts in your classroom or school?

- Use the high-quality texts to develop lessons focusing on other reading domains such as inference, prediction, comparison and explanation.

- Use the texts and question sets to complement your writing units based on the same text. If children have done lots of comprehension activities related to a text, they will have a better overall understanding of the characters, settings and events depicted in the text.

- Use the extracts as ways to hook children into reading new books and genres. If you're using a text that is an extract from a book, have a physical copy of the book available to give to children once they are hooked.

- Rather than reading a whole book, develop writing units based on the short extracts of books or poems so that children gain a greater understanding of a far smaller extract. This is great for interventions or time-sensitive writing opportunities.

AN UNUSUAL CAKE

ADAM BUSHNELL

"Can I help, Dad?" asked Anya.

"Of course!" Dad replied, taking a mixing bowl from the cupboard.

"What do we need?"

"You get the self-raising flour and caster sugar," smiled Dad. "I'll get the margarine and an egg."

"Is this caster sugar?" Anya asked, putting the flour and sugar on the kitchen bench.

"Yes, that's it."

"Anything else?"

"We need cocoa powder and chocolate chips. Do you know where they are?"

Anya nodded, "Of course!"

Dad switched on the electronic scales.

"Measure out 50 grams of caster sugar into a bowl," Dad said. "Then we add 25 grams of margarine."

"25 grams, right."

"Then we cream those together until they're light and fluffy."

"Can we use the mixer please?" Anya asked. "It takes ages with a spoon."

"Of course," smiled Dad as he brought the mixer down from a tall cupboard.

"It's so noisy!" called Anya above the sound of the mixer stirring the ingredients into a creamy, light and fluffy texture.

"What's next?" she asked after her Dad turned the mixer off.

"We add the egg, 50 grams of self-raising flour, 15 grams of cocoa

FICTION: DIALOGUE

powder and 15 grams of chocolate chips and mix it all together."

They measured the ingredients out and Anya then put them in the bowl. The mixer was turned back on.

"Right," Dad smiled. "Now, a courgette!"

"A what?" asked Anya.

"We grate a courgette into the mixture."

"Urgh! That sounds disgusting!"

"Trust me," said Dad.

"This is weird," said Anya, as she grated a whole courgette into the mixture before Dad turned on the mixer.

"Now what?"

"Now we pour the mixture into a greased tin and bake it in the centre of a pre-heated oven at 180^0C for 20 to 25 minutes."

"Is this OK?" asked Anya as she grabbed the tin and margarine.

"Yes," her dad nodded, rubbing the margarine around the inside of the tin.

"It smells lovely!" Anya said as she spooned the mixture into the tin.

After 20 minutes, Dad checked the cake with a skewer.

"It's ready!" she called.

"I can't wait to taste it!"

"Now we wait," said Dad as he put the cake onto a cooling rack.

When the cake was cool, Dad sliced it up.

"I can't believe there's a courgette in this!" Anya gasped as she tasted the cake. "It's really delicious!"

"I have my tricks," laughed Dad.

✏ FILL IN THE GAP

Read the sentences and choose the correct word to fill in each gap.

1 "Of course!" Dad replied, taking a mixing bowl from the _____.

2 "You get the self-raising _____ and caster sugar," smiled Dad.

3 "We need cocoa powder and _____ chips. Do you know where they are?"

4 "Measure out _____ grams of caster sugar into a bowl," Dad said.

5 "It takes ages with a _____."

6 "It's so noisy!" called Anya above the sound of the mixture stirring the _____ into a creamy, light and fluffy texture.

7 "This is weird," said Anya, as she grated a whole _____ into the mixture before Dad turned on the mixer.

8 "Now we pour the mixture into a _____ tin and bake it in the centre of a pre-heated oven at 180⁰C for 20 to 25 minutes."

9 "Is this OK?" asked Anya as she grabbed the tin and _____.

10 "It smells _____!" Anya said as she spooned the mixture into the tin.

11 "It's really _____!"

❓ FIVE Ws AND HOW

Answer the questions below. Look back at *An Unusual Cake* to find the correct answers.

1 What is the name of the character who asks to help?

_____

2 What type of flour is used in the mixture?

_____

3 How many grams of caster sugar are used?

_____

4 How many grams of margarine are used in the mixture?

_____

5 What do they mix the ingredients with?

_____

6 How many eggs are used in the mixture?

_____

7 What temperature is the oven?

_____

8 How long does Dad wait to check the cake?

_____

9 What does Dad check the cake with?

_____

10 When does Dad slice up the cake?

_____

11 What can't Anya believe is in the cake?

_____

12 Who has cooking tricks?

_____

◎ MULTIPLE CHOICE

Circle the correct answer to the following questions.

1 Where is the mixing bowl taken from?

draining board	wardrobe	cupboard	drawer

2 How many eggs are used in the mixture?

1	2	3	4

3 What temperature is the cake baked at?

160°C	170°C	180°C	190°C

4 How long is the cake baked for?

20 to 25 minutes	25 to 30 minutes	30 to 35 minutes	35 to 40 minutes

5 What is the tin greased with?

butter	oil	margarine	coconut oil

6 After how many minutes does Dad check the cake?

10	15	20	25

7 What does Dad check the cake with?

a knife	a thermometer	a fork	a skewer

8 What are Anya and her dad baking?

carrot cake	chocolate cake	cookies	courgette cake

Comprehension Ninja 7-8 © Andrew Jennings, 2021

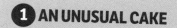 # TRUE OR FALSE

Read the sentences. Put a tick in the correct box to show which sentences are true and which are false.

1 Dad asks Anya to help. True ☐ False ☐

2 The first item taken from the cupboard is a mixing bowl. True ☐ False ☐

3 Three eggs are needed. True ☐ False ☐

4 Anya doesn't know where to find the cocoa powder. True ☐ False ☐

5 The scales are electronic. True ☐ False ☐

6 50 grams of margarine is used. True ☐ False ☐

7 Anya wants to use a spoon to mix with. True ☐ False ☐

8 The mixer is very noisy. True ☐ False ☐

9 The courgette is added to the mixture first. True ☐ False ☐

10 Anya grates half of the courgette. True ☐ False ☐

11 The mixture is baked for 20 to 25 minutes. True ☐ False ☐

12 Anya rubs the tin with margarine. True ☐ False ☐

13 Dad checks the cake with a skewer. True ☐ False ☐

14 Anya slices the cake. True ☐ False ☐

15 The cake tastes disgusting. True ☐ False ☐

✏ SUMMARISE 🏷 DRAW AND LABEL

SUMMARISE

1 Look at the first five lines of the text. Tick the statement which best summarises this section.

Anya tasted the cake when it was ready. ☐

Anya's dad got the mixer out from the cupboard. ☐

Anya started to help her dad find the ingredients. ☐

Anya found out that the cake had courgettes in it. ☐

2 Look at the section beginning 'They measured…' until the end of the text. Write one sentence to summarise what's happening in this section.

_____

_____

DRAW AND LABEL

Draw the statements in the boxes. Add your own labels to your drawings.

Anya using the mixing machine	Dad checking the cake with a skewer

Comprehension Ninja 7-8 © Andrew Jennings, 2021

123 SEQUENCING

1 **Look at the sentence below. Write the numbers 1 to 4 to show the order the words occur in the sentence.**

"It's so noisy!" called Anya above the sound of the mixer stirring the ingredients into a creamy, light and fluffy texture.

ingredients	mixer	noisy	fluffy

2 **Look at the section from 'After 20 minutes…' until the end of the text. Number the sentences from 1 to 5 to show the order they occur in the text.**

"Now we wait," said Dad as he put the cake onto a cooling rack. ☐

When the cake was cool, Dad sliced it up. ☐

"It's ready!" she called. ☐

"I can't wait to taste it!" ☐

"I have my tricks," laughed Dad. ☐

3 **Look at *An Unusual Cake.* Number the sentences from 1 to 5 to show the order they occur in the whole text.**

"We need cocoa powder and chocolate chips. . ." ☐

"Urgh! That sounds disgusting!" ☐

"Measure out 50 grams of caster sugar into a bowl. . ." ☐

"I have my tricks," laughed Dad. ☐

After 20 minutes, Dad checked the cake with a skewer. ☐

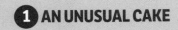

 FIND AND COPY

These questions are about *An Unusual Cake*.

1 Look at the section beginning to read: '"We need cocoa powder. . .'". Find and copy a word that tells us that Anya moved her head up and down.

_____

2 Look at the section beginning 'Dad switched on…'. Find and copy a word that shows that Dad wanted to know the exact amount of caster sugar.

_____

3 Look at the section beginning '"It's so noisy!"'. Find and copy a word that tells us that Anya and her Dad were using many different types of food in the recipe.

_____

4 Look at the section beginning '"Now we pour the mixture…"'. Find and copy a word that means that margarine has been rubbed in the tin to stop the cake from sticking.

_____

5 Look at the section beginning '"It smells lovely!"' Find and copy a word that tells us that Anya used a spoon.

_____

6 Look at the section beginning '"When the cake was cool…'. Find and copy a word that tells us that Dad cut the cake.

_____

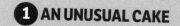

✏ CIRCLE A WORD

Read the paragraphs below and then follow the instructions.

"It's so noisy!" called Anya above the sound of the mixer stirring the ingredients into a creamy, light and fluffy texture.

"What's next?" she asked after her Dad turned the mixer off.

"We add the egg, 50 grams of self-raising flour, 15 grams of cocoa powder and 15 grams of chocolate chips and mix it all together."

1 Circle a word that means that something is making a lot of sound.

2 Circle a word that means that something is soft, light and contains air.

3 Circle a word that means how something looks or feels.

4 Circle a word that means fine, dry particles.

5 Circle a word that means to combine or put together.

MAUII AND THE SUN

ADAM BUSHNELL

A very long time ago the sun did not travel slowly across the sky like it does today. It would race across the sky at top speed. Everyone was unhappy because the night time was very, very long and the day time was very, very short.

Mauii, the hero, decided he would catch the sun and ask it to travel slowly across the sky. So, he collected coconuts, pulled the hairs from the coconut shells and then plaited them together into a really long rope.

Mauii rowed in a boat out to the edge of the ocean and waited for the sun. When the sun came racing across the sky, Mauii threw the rope and caught the sun. But the sun pulled and sizzled through the rope, then plunged into the ocean.

Mauii looked really angry as he rowed the boat back to the beach.

Mauii decided to collect all of the coconuts from the whole island. Then he pulled the hairs from the coconut shells and plaited them together into a really long, really strong rope.

Mauii rowed to the edge of the ocean. When the sun came racing across the sky, Mauii threw the rope and caught the sun. But, again, the sun pulled and sizzled through the rope then plunged into the ocean.

Mauii decided to visit his sister, Hina.

"Oh Hina," said Mauii. "With your long, magical and beautiful hair . . . Can I cut it all off please?"

"NO WAY!!!!" shouted Hina. "You're not cutting all my hair off!"

"Oh but Hina, with your long, magical and beautiful hair, we could make a long, magical and beautiful rope and use it to catch the sun."

"Oh . . . alright then," said Hina. Mauii cut off Hina's hair and plaited it into a long, magical and beautiful rope. Then he and his sister rowed in the boat out to the edge of the ocean. When the sun came racing across the sky, Mauii and Hina threw the rope and caught the sun.

The sun pulled and tried to sizzle through the rope but it couldn't.

"LET ME GO!" said the sun. But Mauii and Hina called, "Not until you promise to travel slowly across the sky every day!"
"I PROMISE," said the sun. "NOW LET ME GO!"

Mauii and Hina let go of the rope and the sun travelled slowly into the ocean.

The next morning, the sun rose slowly out of the ocean, travelled slowly across the sky and set slowly into the ocean again. As it does every day, all thanks to Mauii and Hina.

✏ FILL IN THE GAP

Read the sentences and choose the correct word to fill in each gap.

1 A very long time ago the sun did not _____ slowly across the sky like it does today.

2 It would race across the _____ at top speed.

3 Everyone was _____ because the night time was very, very long and the day time was very, very short.

4 Mauii rowed in a boat out to the edge of the _____ and waited for the sun.

5 When the sun came racing across the sky, _____ threw the rope and caught the sun.

6 But the sun pulled and sizzled through the _____, then plunged into the ocean.

7 Mauii decided to collect all of the _____ from the whole island.

8 When the sun came racing across the sky, Mauii threw the rope and caught the _____.

9 But, again, the sun pulled and sizzled through the rope then _____ into the ocean.

10 Mauii cut off Hina's hair and _____ it into a long, magical and beautiful rope.

11 The next morning, the sun rose slowly out of the _____, travelled slowly across the sky and set slowly into the ocean again.

12 As it does every day, all _____ to Mauii and Hina.

 Comprehension Ninja 7-8 © Andrew Jennings, 2021

? FIVE Ws AND HOW

Answer the questions below. Look back at *Mauii and the Sun* to find the correct answers.

1 What speed does the sun race across the sky at the start of the story?

_____

2 How does everyone feel about the situation?

_____

3 What part of the day is very, very long at the start of the story?

_____

4 What does Mauii decide he would ask the sun?

_____

5 What does Mauii collect?

_____

6 What does Mauii make with the coconut hairs?

_____

7 What does Mauii wait for at the edge of the ocean?

_____

8 How does the sun get free from the rope?

_____

9 Who is Hina?

_____

10 What does Mauii ask Hina for?

_____

11 What does Hina refuse to allow Mauii to do at first?

_____

12 What does the sun promise to do?

_____

 MULTIPLE CHOICE

Circle the correct answer to the following questions.

1 When is the story set?

| not long ago | a long time ago | a few days ago | a very long time ago |

2 How long are the nights at the start of the story?

| very, very long | really short | quite short | 4 hours |

3 What does Mauii want to ask the sun to do?

| shine brighter | travel slowly | move faster | not shine so brightly |

4 What is the first rope made from?

| magical hair | leaves | coconuts | vines |

5 What does Mauii do with the coconut hairs?

| weaves them | plaits them | knots them | ties them |

6 Where does Mauii row to?

| the edge of the ocean | the middle of the ocean | the deepest part of the ocean | the closest part of the ocean |

7 What is Mauii and Hina's relationship?

| husband and wife | best friends | brother and sister | friends |

8 What does Hina say when Mauii first asks to cut off her hair?

| "Of course!" | "Why?" | "I'd be happy to let you." | "No way!" |

👍 TRUE OR FALSE

Read the sentences. Put a tick in the correct box to show which sentences are true and which are false.

1 Everyone is unhappy because the night is very long.　　True ☐　False ☐

2 Mauii is a hero.　　True ☐　False ☐

3 Hina decides to catch the sun.　　True ☐　False ☐

4 Mauii ties the coconuts in knots to make a rope.　　True ☐　False ☐

5 Mauii uses a ladder to catch the sun.　　True ☐　False ☐

6 Mauii collects all of the coconuts from the island.　　True ☐　False ☐

7 Mauii makes a rope from coconut hair.　　True ☐　False ☐

8 Mauii rows a boat to the edge of the ocean.　　True ☐　False ☐

9 The sun sizzles through the coconut hair rope.　　True ☐　False ☐

10 Mauii has magical hair.　　True ☐　False ☐

11 Hina cuts off Mauii's hair.　　True ☐　False ☐

12 Hina's hair is short.　　True ☐　False ☐

13 Mauii and Hina catch the sun with Hina's magical hair.　　True ☐　False ☐

14 The sun sizzles through Hina's magical hair.　　True ☐　False ☐

15 The sun promises to travel slowly.　　True ☐　False ☐

SUMMARISE  DRAW AND LABEL

SUMMARISE

1 **Look at the paragraph beginning 'Mauii rowed…'. Tick the statement which best summarises this paragraph.**

The sun was too fast for Mauii to catch it. ☐

Mauii caught the sun with the rope. ☐

The sun was too hot for Mauii to get close to it. ☐

Mauii caught the sun with the rope, but the sun burned through it. ☐

2 **Look at the conversation between Mauii and Hina, beginning 'Mauii decided to see…'. Write one sentence to summarise what's happening in this conversation.**

_____

_____

DRAW AND LABEL

Draw the statements in the boxes. Add your own labels to your drawings.

Mauii rowed in a boat out to the edge of the ocean.	But the sun pulled and sizzled through the rope.

123 SEQUENCING

1 **Look at the sentence below. Write the numbers 1 to 4 to show the order the words occur in the sentence.**

So, he collected coconuts, pulled the hairs from the coconut shells and then plaited them together into a really long rope.

rope	hairs	collected	plaited

2 **Look at the section beginning 'Mauii looked really angry…'. Number the sentences from 1 to 5 to show the order they occur in the text.**

Then he pulled the hairs from the coconut shells and plaited them together into a really long, really strong rope. ☐

Mauii rowed to the edge of the ocean. ☐

Mauii looked really angry as he rowed the boat back to the beach. ☐

When the sun came racing across the sky, Mauii threw the rope and caught the sun. ☐

Mauii decided to collect all of the coconuts from the whole island. ☐

3 **Look at *Mauii and the Sun*. Number the sentences from 1 to 5 to show the order they occur in the whole text. Look at the first line of each paragraph to help you.**

A very long time ago the sun did not travel slowly across the sky like it does today. ☐

Mauii looked really angry as he rowed the boat back to the beach. ☐

Mauii, the hero, decided he would catch the sun and ask it to travel slowly across the sky. ☐

Mauii rowed in a boat out to the edge of the ocean and waited for the sun. ☐

Mauii decided to visit his sister, Hina. ☐

FIND AND COPY

These questions are about _Mauii and the Sun_.

1 Look at the first paragraph. Find and copy a word that shows that the sun was moving quickly.

_____

2 Look at the paragraph beginning 'Mauii, the hero…'. Find and copy a word that suggests that Mauii was admired for his courage.

_____

3 Look at the paragraph beginning 'Mauii rowed in a boat…'. Find and copy a word that shows that Mauii stopped the sun from moving and held it.

_____

4 Look at the paragraph beginning 'Mauii rowed in a boat…'. Find and copy a word that shows that the sun was very hot.

_____

5 Look at the paragraph beginning '"Oh . . . alright then," said Hina.'. Find and copy a word that tells us that the rope was pretty.

_____

6 Look at the paragraph beginning '"LET ME GO!" said the sun.'. Find and copy a word that tells us that Mauii and Hina shouted.

_____

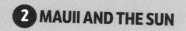

✎ CIRCLE A WORD

Read the paragraphs below and then follow the instructions.

Mauii looked really angry as he rowed the boat back to the beach.

Mauii decided to collect all of the coconuts from the whole island. Then he pulled the hairs from the coconut shells and plaited them together into a really long, really strong rope.

Mauii rowed to the edge of the ocean. When the sun came racing across the sky, Mauii threw the rope and caught the sun. But, again, the sun pulled and sizzled through the rope then plunged into the ocean.

1 Circle a word that means to be annoyed and upset.

2 Circle a word that means the outside limit of an area.

3 Circle a word that means a very large body of water.

4 Circle a word that means moving fast or swiftly.

5 Circle a word that means dived or fell quickly.

STONE AGE GIRL

ADAM BUSHNELL

The girl looked around her community. It was based next to the river and was bustling with activity. On the river bank a man was using a flint axe to carve the slats for a canoe. Some ducks idly swam past, unaware that a hunter was taking aim with a flint arrow. His bow was bending as he pulled at the reed string. With a whoosh the arrow flew and hit its target. The hunter then waded into the river and collected a dead duck.

Further along the river there were people fishing. One person was using a net and the others had wooden spears.

Behind the girl was a row of tents. They were made with long wooden poles that formed a pyramid shape. Then animal hide was stretched over the outside. The raw hide was tough and waterproof. Then mud and plants were smoothed over the outside of the tent to make the inside warm and cosy. There was no one in the tents though. Everyone had a job to do.

Some children had raced down to the river to see the duck that had been killed. The hunter handed the duck to the children and they began to pluck it. A dog padded up to them looking at the duck with hungry eyes.

The girl stood up and walked away from the river and along the line of tents. She passed a flint worker who was teaching his son how to carve the stones into different shapes for different uses. The boy was using a hand axe to chip off smaller pieces of flint from a large piece to make arrow heads for the hunters.

She then passed the storyteller sitting by a large fire. She was telling the tales of the community's ancestors to some children who sat enthralled.

There was the sound of flint on wood in the distance. The woodcutter was always busy.

She should be busy too. It was her job to gather berries. She carried a bag made from rabbit skin. It felt warm and soft in her hand. She looked up and saw the lookout in a tall tree. It was his job to watch for any dangerous animals coming out of the forest. But with their dogs and the fires that always burned, mostly the community was left alone.

As the girl entered the woods she was submerged in almost total darkness. Her eyes soon adjusted to the lack of light, and she found some blackberries.

As she placed them in her bag, a twig snapped behind her and she turned to see a huge boar. Its razor-sharp tusks were pointing at her.

✏ FILL IN THE GAP

Read the sentences and choose the correct word to fill in each gap.

1 His bow was bending as he pulled at the _____ string.

2 The hunter then _____ into the river and collected a dead duck.

3 Behind the _____ was a row of tents.

4 They were made with long wooden poles that formed a _____ shape.

5 The raw hide was tough and _____.

6 Then mud and plants were _____ over the outside of the tent to make the inside warm and cosy.

7 There was no one in the _____ though.

8 It was her job to gather _____.

9 She carried a bag made from _____ skin.

10 She looked up and saw the _____ in a tall tree.

11 It was his job to watch for any _____ animals coming out of the forest.

12 But with their dogs and the fires that always _____, mostly the community was left alone.

                                     Comprehension Ninja 7-8 © Andrew Jennings, 2021

? FIVE Ws AND HOW

Answer the questions below. Look back at *Stone Age Girl* to find the correct answers.

1 What is the community based next to?

_____

2 What is the man using to carve the slats for a canoe?

_____

3 What are swimming idly by the hunter?

_____

4 What is the string of the bow made from?

_____

5 What are the people further along the river doing?

_____

6 What shape are the tents?

_____

7 What is stretched over the outside of the tents?

_____

8 What are the children racing down to the river to see?

_____

9 Who is sitting by the large fire?

_____

10 Where can the sound of flint on wood be heard?

_____

11 What is the girl's job?

_____

12 Where is the lookout?

_____

◉ MULTIPLE CHOICE

Circle the correct answer to the following questions.

1 What are the children plucking?

| goose | duck | chicken | pheasant |

2 What is the storyteller sat beside?

| the river | the pyramid tent | the woods | a large fire |

3 What is the girl's bag made from?

| reeds | twigs and leaves | wool | rabbit skin |

4 Where is the lookout positioned?

| in the bushes | by the front gate | by the pyramid tents | in a tall tree |

5 As well as the fire, what is the other reason why dangerous animals leave the villagers alone?

| weapons | lookout | dogs | human noises |

6 What type of berries are collected by the girl?

| strawberries | blueberries | raspberries | blackberries |

7 What snaps behind the girl as she puts the blackberries in her bag?

| a flower | a twig | kindling | a leaf |

8 What is the animal with large razor-sharp tusks?

| pig | elephant | boar | goat |

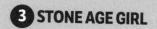

TRUE OR FALSE

Read the sentences. Put a tick in the correct box to show which sentences are true and which are false.

1 The community is in the middle of the desert.　　True ☐　False ☐

2 The hunter kills a duck.　　True ☐　False ☐

3 Nets and spears are used to fish.　　True ☐　False ☐

4 Animal hides help to waterproof the tents.　　True ☐　False ☐

5 Only certain people have jobs to do.　　True ☐　False ☐

6 Children are plucking the duck.　　True ☐　False ☐

7 The storyteller is sat by the fire.　　True ☐　False ☐

8 The storyteller tells stories of their ancestors.　　True ☐　False ☐

9 The girl's job is to be a lookout.　　True ☐　False ☐

10 Dangerous animals are always coming onto their land.　　True ☐　False ☐

11 The girl's bag is made from reeds and leaves.　　True ☐　False ☐

12 The woods are very dark.　　True ☐　False ☐

13 The girl is picking blackberries.　　True ☐　False ☐

14 A twig snaps behind the girl.　　True ☐　False ☐

15 A bear with sharp claws is stood behind her.　　True ☐　False ☐

SUMMARISE DRAW AND LABEL

SUMMARISE

1 **Look at the paragraph beginning 'The girl entered the woods…'. Tick the statement which best summarises this paragraph.**

The girl is picking berries in the woods. ☐

The woods are light, and the girl can't find any berries. ☐

The girl enters the dark woods and is confronted by a boar. ☐

The girl is acting as a lookout. ☐

2 **Look at the paragraph beginning 'She should be busy…'. Write one sentence to summarise what's happening in this paragraph.**

_____

_____

DRAW AND LABEL

Draw the statements in the boxes. Add your own labels to your drawings.

Further along the river there were people fishing.	She turned to see a huge boar. Its razor-sharp tusks were pointed at her.

⑫③ SEQUENCING

1 **Look at the sentence below. Write the numbers 1 to 4 to show the order the words occur in the sentence.**

Then mud and plants were smoothed over the outside of the tent to make the inside warm and cosy.

inside	plants	mud	outside

2 **Look at the paragraph beginning 'She should be busy...'. Number the sentences from 1 to 5 to show the order they occur in the text.**

It was his job to watch for any dangerous animals coming out of the forest. ☐

But with their dogs and the fires that always burned, mostly the community was left alone. ☐

It was her job to gather berries. ☐

She carried a bag made from rabbit skin. ☐

She looked up and saw the lookout in a tall tree. ☐

3 **Look at *Stone Age Girl*. Number the sentences from 1 to 5 to show the order they occur in the whole text. Look at the first line of each paragraph to help you.**

There was the sound of flint on wood in the distance. ☐

The girl stood up and walked away from the river and along the line of tents. ☐

As she placed them in her bag, a twig snapped behind her and she turned to see a huge boar. ☐

The girl looked around her community. ☐

Behind the girl was a row of tents. ☐

 FIND AND COPY

These questions are about *Stone Age Girl*.

1 Look at the first paragraph. Find and copy a word that shows that the ducks didn't know an arrow was being aimed at them.

_____

2 Look at the paragraph beginning 'Behind the girl was…'. Find and copy a word that tells us that the hide was strong.

_____

3 Look at the paragraph beginning 'Some children had raced…'. Find and copy a word that means that the children pulled feathers out of the duck.

_____

4 Look at the paragraph beginning 'She then passed the storyteller…'. Find and copy a word that shows that the children were very interested and enjoying the stories.

_____

5 Look at the paragraph beginning 'As the girl entered the woods…'. Find and copy a word that tells us that there is hardly any light.

_____

6 Look at the last paragraph. Find and copy a word that tells us that a twig broke.

_____

✎ CIRCLE A WORD

Read the paragraphs below and then follow the instructions.

The girl stood up and walked away from the river and along the line of tents. She passed a flint worker who was teaching his son how to carve the stones into different shapes for different uses. The boy was using a hand axe to chip off smaller pieces of flint from a large piece to make arrow heads for the hunters.

She then passed the storyteller sitting by a large fire. She was telling the tales of the community's ancestors to some children who sat enthralled.

1 Circle a word that means to shape a material.

2 Circle a word that means people who find and kill animals for food.

3 Circle a word that means a person who tells stories.

3 Circle a word that means stories.

4 Circle a word that tells us that the children were fascinated by the stories.

THE LOST TOMB

ADAM BUSHNELL

A temple guardian stood outside the pyramid. Amir looked at the statue and smiled. This would be his greatest adventure.

He slipped past the statue and entered the darkness of the pyramid. After lighting a flaming torch, he scanned the path before him. He needed to be careful. There would be traps everywhere. Amir had explored many pyramids before but each was different from the last. You never knew if one wrong step could send you tumbling into pits of lava or spikes. You had to be careful.

The flickering light of his torch illuminated the floor and walls. Large hieroglyphs were painted on either side and Amir took his time to read them. There were often clues located in the pictures. Thoth, the god of wisdom, was Amir's guide. It was better to choose a path of wisdom rather than racing in foolhardily.

There was a hieroglyph of a man falling. Amir stopped. He pressed the floor in front of him with one foot. Then pressed another section of the floor. After repeating this several times, he had only moved forward a few paces.

As he pushed his foot down again, the ground suddenly crumbled and fell. Amir jumped backwards. There was a hole in the path ahead of him. He couldn't see the bottom. Amir pressed his back against the wall and slid forward along the narrow ledge that was left.

After passing the hole, Amir continued to test the floor in front of him and read the hieroglyphs for more clues. There was an image of a man bowing low and another of an axe.

FICTION: ADVENTURE

Amir didn't need telling twice. He crawled forwards on his hands and knees. As he did so the walls split open and axe heads came spinning from either side. They landed with heavy thuds thankfully far above Amir's head.

He let out a long breath and continued on his journey, still testing the floor and reading the walls.

The path turned a corner. There were more hieroglyphs; this time showing hooded snakes. Amir stopped. His eyes scanned the floor and walls again. He stepped forward slowly. Suddenly something fell from above. Cobras! A whole nest of cobra snakes had been tipped from above. Amir realised that one was coiled across his shoulders, others were sliding over his legs. One wrong move and they would strike. These venomous snakes were lethal. Amir shrugged his shoulders gently and the cobra fell to the floor. He slowly moved the flaming torch towards his legs and the other cobras retreated away from the flames. He stepped away with eyes wide and heart thumping.

When he looked up, he realised that he was in the centre of the pyramid. He had made it!

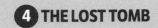

✏ FILL IN THE GAP

Read the sentences and choose the correct word to fill in each gap.

1 A temple guardian stood outside the _____.

2 After lighting a _____ torch, he scanned the path before him.

3 You never knew if one wrong step could send you _____ into pits of lava or spikes.

4 Large _____ were painted on either side and Amir took his time to read them.

5 It was better to choose a path of wisdom rather than racing in _____.

6 After _____ this several times, he had only moved forward a few paces.

7 There was an image of a man _____ low and another of an axe.

8 As he did so the walls split open and _____ heads came spinning from either side.

9 He let out a long breath and continued on his _____, still testing the floor and reading the walls.

10 Amir realised that one was coiled across his _____, others were sliding over his legs.

11 He slowly moved the flaming torch towards his legs and the other _____ retreated away from the flames.

12 When he looked up, he realised that he was in the _____ of the pyramid.

❓ FIVE Ws AND HOW

Answer the questions below. Look back at *The Lost Tomb* to find the correct answers.

1 What does Amir see stood outside of the pyramid?

_____

2 What does Amir light to help him see the path before him?

_____

3 What does Amir need to be careful of?

_____

4 Where might one wrong step take you?

_____

5 Where are large hieroglyphs painted?

_____

6 Who is the god of wisdom?

_____

7 What part of his body does Amir use to press the floor in front of him?

_____

8 What image is shown with the image of the man bowing low?

_____

9 Which parts of his body does Amir use after reading the hieroglyphs?

_____

10 Where do the spinning axe heads come from?

_____

11 What creatures fall from above?

_____

12 What does Amir use to force the snakes back?

_____

◉ MULTIPLE CHOICE

Circle the correct answer to the following questions.

1 What is stood outside the pyramid?

| a temple guardian | a centaur guardian | a pyramid guardian | a spirit guardian |

2 What does Amir use to light the darkness of the pyramid?

| a mobile phone | a flaming torch | a gas lamp | an electric torch |

3 If you take one wrong step, you might tumble into pits filled with what?

| fire or cobras | spiders or arrows | snakes or axes | lava or spikes |

4 Who is the god of wisdom?

| Wroth | Broth | Thoth | Groth |

5 What does the second set of hieroglyphs show?

| a man bowing low and an axe | a man praying to the gods | a man pointing and snakes | a man falling |

6 What creatures are tipped from above?

| rabbits | spiders | ants | cobras |

7 What word is used to describe the venomous snakes?

| dangerous | lethal | deadly | fatal |

8 Where does Amir reach at the end of the story?

| the end of the pyramid | a hidden chamber | the centre of the pyramid | the exit |

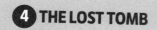 # TRUE OR FALSE

Read the sentences. Put a tick in the correct box to show which sentences are true and which are false.

1 Many temple guardians are stood outside the pyramid. True ☐ False ☐

2 Amir uses a battery-powered torch to light the darkness. True ☐ False ☐

3 This is the first pyramid Amir has explored. True ☐ False ☐

4 One wrong step could send you into pits of lava or spikes. True ☐ False ☐

5 Amir looks at hieroglyphs for clues. True ☐ False ☐

6 Thoth is the god of wisdom. True ☐ False ☐

7 Amir uses a map as a guide. True ☐ False ☐

8 Amir ignores the warnings written in the hieroglyphs. True ☐ False ☐

9 Amir crawls on his hands and knees to avoid axe heads. True ☐ False ☐

10 A whole nest of snakes is tipped onto Amir. True ☐ False ☐

11 The cobras are venomous. True ☐ False ☐

12 The cobras retreat away from the flames. True ☐ False ☐

13 Amir is bitten by one of the snakes. True ☐ False ☐

14 The pyramid has no traps. True ☐ False ☐

15 Amir didn't find the centre of the pyramid. True ☐ False ☐

✏ SUMMARISE ✏ DRAW AND LABEL

SUMMARISE

1 **Look at the paragraph beginning 'As he pushed his foot…'. Tick the statement which best summarises this paragraph.**

Amir falls into a hole as the floor crumbled away. ☐

Axe heads fly above Amir's head. ☐

The floor crumbles and a hole appears in the path, but Amir avoids it. ☐

Amir falls into the hole and ducks down as the hieroglyphs told him to do. ☐

2 **Look at the paragraph beginning 'The path turned a corner.'. Write one sentence to summarise what's happening in this paragraph.**

_____

_____

DRAW AND LABEL

Draw the statements in the boxes. Add your own labels to your drawings.

One wrong step could send you tumbling into pits of lava or spikes.	A whole nest of cobra snakes had been tipped from above.

123 SEQUENCING

1 **Look at the sentences below. Write the numbers 1 to 4 to show the order the words occur in the sentences.**

He stepped away with eyes wide and heart thumping.
When he looked up, he realised that he was in the centre of the pyramid.

pyramid	thumping	realised	wide

2 **Look at the paragraph beginning 'The path turned a corner.'. Number the sentences from 1 to 5 to show the order they occur in the text.**

A whole nest of cobra snakes had been tipped from above.

There were more hieroglyphs; this time showing hooded snakes.

His eyes scanned the floor and walls again.

Amir realised that one was coiled across his shoulders, others were sliding over his legs.

Amir shrugged his shoulders gently and the cobra fell to the floor.

3 **Look at *The Lost Tomb*. Number the sentences from 1 to 5 to show the order they occur in the whole text. Look at the last line of each paragraph to help you.**

This would be his greatest adventure.

They landed with heavy thuds thankfully far from Amir's head.

You had to be careful.

He had made it!

He stepped away with eyes wide and heart thumping.

 FIND AND COPY

These questions are about _The Lost Tomb_.

1 Look at the paragraph beginning 'He slipped past…'. Find and copy a word that tells us that there are mechanisms designed to trap people in the pyramid.

_____

2 Look at the paragraph beginning 'The flickering light…'. Find and copy a word that tells us that there are things to help Amir in the hieroglyphs.

_____

3 Look at the paragraph beginning 'There was a hieroglyph…'. Find and copy a word that tells us that Amir stood still.

_____

4 Look at the paragraph beginning 'As he pushed his foot…'. Find and copy a word that tells us that the path isn't very wide.

_____

5 Look at the paragraph beginning 'Amir didn't need telling…'. Find and copy a word that tells us that the axe heads made a noise when they landed.

_____

6 Look at the paragraph beginning 'The path turned…'. Find and copy a word that tells us that Amir carefully and slowly shrugged his shoulders.

_____

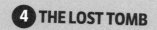 CIRCLE A WORD

Read the paragraphs below and then follow the instructions.

Amir realised that one was coiled across his shoulders, others were sliding over his legs. One wrong move and they would strike. These venomous snakes were lethal. Amir shrugged his shoulders gently and the cobra fell to the floor. He slowly moved the flaming torch towards his legs and the other cobras retreated away from the flames. He stepped away with eyes wide and heart thumping.

When he looked up, he realised that he was in the centre of the pyramid. He had made it!

1 Circle a word that means twisted around.

2 Circle a word that means to attack quickly.

3 Circle a word that means harmful enough to kill someone.

4 Circle a word that means to raise and flick your shoulder.

5 Circle a word that means moved away.

THE TIME PORTAL

ADAM BUSHNELL

As she stepped up to the portal it shimmered. The doorway was like water and moved constantly. The frame that surrounded it was a mass of wires, switches and buttons. Lights flickered and flashed.

She was ready. She had tested the portal on short journeys many times before. She had used it to travel backwards five minutes and forwards ten minutes. Now she wanted to put it to a real test. She wanted to see if she could go deep into the past and far into the future.

She nodded to her assistant, who nodded back then furrowed his brow as he concentrated on the screen.

"Ready, Jenkins?"

The assistant nodded.

"I think so," Jenkins replied. "All systems look good to go. One hundred years to the day."

"Good."

The lights around the portal's doorway flickered again then turned to a constant green. The woman took a step forward.

"See you soon," she called as she entered the portal.

Jenkins watched as the scientist was engulfed by the fluid of the portal. Then she was gone.

The scientist gasped at the sight before her. A huge creature stomped nearby. It towered above her, its long neck reaching up towards impossibly tall trees. It took a long snap at the leaves and crunched noisily. It was a dinosaur!

More dinosaurs roamed nearby: a huge herd of around a hundred of them. The scientist recognised them to be sauropods, and the dinosaur near her was part of the herd. It took another large mouthful of leaves then lopped off to join the herd it had wandered away from.

These were plant-eating dinosaurs, but what if a carnivore was nearby?

She turned back to the portal and stepped inside. She was instantly back in the laboratory.

"How long was I gone?" she asked Jenkins.

"About two seconds!" gasped the assistant. "How was it?"

"I went too far. It was the Jurassic period."

Jenkins gasped. The scientist ran over to the control panel and made some adjustments.

"Let's try again," she said at last.

"Are you sure?"

The scientist didn't reply. She stepped back to the portal. Jenkins pressed buttons and the flickering green lights on the portal turned a solid green again.

"Good luck!" Jenkins called.

The scientist stepped into the portal's doorway and was gone again. When she emerged on the other side she gasped for a second time.

A group of people were pointing and staring at her. They wore animal skins in strips over their bodies. One of them grabbed her, and the others started to prod and poke at the portal with their spears.

"No, wait!" cried the scientist. "Stop! If you break it I'll never get home!"

✏️ FILL IN THE GAP

Read the sentences and choose the correct word to fill in each gap.

1 As she stepped up to the portal it _____.

2 The doorway was like _____ and moved constantly.

3 The frame that surrounded it was a mass of _____, switches and buttons.

4 She had tested the _____ on short journeys many times before.

5 She had used it to _____ backwards five minutes and forwards ten minutes.

6 She wanted to see if she could go _____ into the past and far into the future.

7 She nodded to her assistant, who nodded back then _____ his brow as he concentrated on the screen.

8 The lights around the _____ doorway flickered again then turned to a constant green.

9 More dinosaurs roamed nearby: a huge herd of around a _____ of them.

10 These were _____-eating dinosaurs, but what if a carnivore was nearby?

11 She was instantly back in the _____.

12 The scientist ran over to the control panel and made some _____.

❓ FIVE Ws AND HOW

Answer the questions below. Look back at _The Time Portal_ to find the correct answers.

1 What is the doorway like?

_____

2 How far backwards had the scientist travelled in tests?

_____

3 How far forwards had the scientist travelled in the tests?

_____

4 What is the scientist's assistant's name?

_____

5 How many years is she planning to go back?

_____

6 What constant colour does the light around the doorway turn after flickering?

_____

7 What animal does the scientist see the first time she travels in time?

_____

8 What type of dinosaur does the scientist recognise?

_____

9 What type of dinosaur is the scientist worried could be nearby?

_____

10 Who makes the adjustments to the control panel?

_____

11 What are the people wearing during the scientist's second time journey?

_____

12 Who grabs the scientist?

_____

◎ MULTIPLE CHOICE

Circle the correct answer to the following questions.

1 What do the lights do in the first paragraph?

| flickered and flamed | shone and shined | flickered and flashed | beamed and boomed |

2 How long does the scientist travel backwards for in the tests?

| five minutes | five hours | five days | five years |

3 How long does the scientist travel forwards for in the tests?

| ten seconds | ten minutes | ten hours | ten days |

4 What happens as the scientist steps into the portal?

| she disappears instantly | there is an explosion | she is engulfed by fluid | there are fireworks |

5 What feature does the dinosaur the scientist first sees have?

| enormous eyes | huge teeth | long neck | powerful legs |

6 What does the scientist recognise the herd of dinosaurs to be?

| carnivores | omnivores | sauropods | triceratops |

7 How long had the scientist been away in the portal?

| two seconds | two minutes | two hours | two days |

8 What do the people prod the portal with?

| sticks | bows and arrows | spears | rocks |

 Comprehension Ninja 7-8 © Andrew Jennings, 2021

👎 TRUE OR FALSE

Read the sentences. Put a tick in the correct box to show which sentences are true and which are false.

1 The doorway is like electricity. True ☐ False ☐

2 Wires, switches and buttons surround the portal's frame. True ☐ False ☐

3 The assistant is a man. True ☐ False ☐

4 The portal has never been tested before. True ☐ False ☐

5 The scientist has already travelled forward fifty minutes. True ☐ False ☐

6 Jenkins sets the portal to two hundred years to the day. True ☐ False ☐

7 The scientist is a woman. True ☐ False ☐

8 Jenkins is the name of the assistant. True ☐ False ☐

9 The scientist only sees one dinosaur. True ☐ False ☐

10 The scientist is with the dinosaurs for about three hours. True ☐ False ☐

11 The dinosaur nearest the scientist is part of a herd. True ☐ False ☐

12 Carnivorous dinosaurs are all around the scientist. True ☐ False ☐

13 The scientist travels to the sauropod period. True ☐ False ☐

14 The people are wearing vines and leaves. True ☐ False ☐

15 People smash the portal to pieces. True ☐ False ☐

SUMMARISE ✏ DRAW AND LABEL

SUMMARISE

1 **Look at the section from "Good luck!" until the end of the text. Tick the statement which best summarises this section.**

The scientist enters the portal and can't return. ☐

The scientist encounters a group of aggressive people. ☐

The machine is broken by the group of people. ☐

The scientist saw a group of people then returns through the portal. ☐

2 **Look at the paragraph beginning 'The scientist gasped…'. Write one sentence to summarise what's happening in this paragraph.**

_____

_____

DRAW AND LABEL

Draw the statements in the boxes. Add your own labels to your drawings.

the frame surrounding the doorway, with wires, switches and buttons	the dinosaur with its long neck, eating leaves

123 SEQUENCING

1 **Look at the sentences below. Write the numbers 1 to 4 to show the order the words occur in the sentences.**

It towered above her, its long neck reaching up towards impossibly tall trees. It took a long snap at the leaves and crunched noisily.

crunched	towered	impossibly	reaching

2 **Look at the paragraph beginning 'She was ready.'. Number the sentences from 1 to 5 to show the order they occur in the text.**

She had used it to travel backwards five minutes and forwards ten minutes. ☐

Now she wanted to put it to a real test. ☐

She had tested the portal on short journeys many times before. ☐

She wanted to see if she could go deep into the past and far into the future. ☐

She was ready. ☐

3 **Look at *The Time Portal*. Number the sentences from 1 to 5 to show the order they occur in the whole text. Look at the first line of each paragraph to help you.**

More dinosaurs roamed nearby: a huge herd of around a hundred of them. ☐

She nodded to her assistant, who nodded back then furrowed his brow as he concentrated on the screen. ☐

The scientist gasped at the sight before her. ☐

A group of people were pointing and staring at her. ☐

As she stepped up to the portal it shimmered. ☐

FIND AND COPY

These questions are about _The Time Portal_.

1 Look at the first paragraph. Find and copy a word that tells us that the doorway of the portal, described as being like water, never stopped moving.

_____

2 Look at the paragraph beginning 'She was ready'. Find and copy a word that tells us that the scientist had only used the portal for small trips.

_____

3 Look at the paragraph beginning 'Jenkins watched…'. Find and copy a word that means that the fluid of the portal completely covered the scientist.

_____

4 Look at the paragraph beginning 'More dinosaurs roamed nearby…'. Find and copy a word that tells us that the dinosaurs were the same species and in a group.

_____

5 Look at the paragraph beginning 'These were plant-eating…'. Find and copy a word that means meat-eating.

_____

6 Look at the paragraph beginning 'The scientist didn't reply'. Find and copy a word that tells us that the lights had stopped flickering.

_____

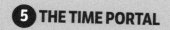

CIRCLE A WORD

Read the paragraph below and then follow the instructions.

> The scientist gasped at the sight before her. A huge creature stomped nearby. It towered above her, its long neck reaching up towards impossibly tall trees. It took a long snap at the leaves and crunched noisily. It was a dinosaur!

1 Circle a word that means to catch your breath in astonishment.

2 Circle a word that means walked with heavy feet.

3 Circle a word that means to be a great height.

4 Circle a word that means beyond belief or unlikely.

5 Circle a word that means loudly.

Home from the Sea from Short! A book of Very Short Stories by Kevin Crossley-Holland© Kevin Crossley-Holland 1998.
Reproduced with permission of Oxford Publishing Limited through PLSclear
Comprehension Ninja 7-8 © Andrew Jennings, 2021

HOME FROM THE SEA

KEVIN CROSSLEY-HOLLAND

On Saturday morning, Jack went down to the creek. To do a bit of crabbing. To nose around in the flotsam and jetsam, and see what the tide had thrown up.

'You keep away from the edge!' said his mum. 'Right away! As if I hadn't got enough to worry about. No money! No food!'

When he rounded the corner of the Maltings, Jack saw a man sitting at one end of the jetty. That's where the little fishing-boats tied up and unloaded their lobsters and flip-flapping shiners. Well, where they used to tie up! Jack's father had been the last fisherman in those parts, but now he was drowned and food for fishes.

'Morning!' said Jack.

But the man did not reply. He didn't even look up.

'Morning!' Jack said again. Then the man did look up. He had strings of seaweed and pieces of scruff and straw tangled up in his beard and hair. And he was wearing thigh boots and an old jersey the sea had starched and decorated with wavy patterns. Jack looked at the man's face and hands. They were white and bloated – like overcooked potatoes. In fact, they looked as if they'd burst if you poked them.

Home from the Sea from Short! A book of Very Short Stories by Kevin Crossley-Holland© Kevin Crossley-Holland 1998.
Reproduced with permission of Oxford Publishing Limited through PLSclear
Comprehension Ninja 7-8 © Andrew Jennings, 2021

FICTION: EXTRACT

Jack gripped his crabbing-stick and pail, and took half-a-step backwards. Then he took another. And then he turned and walked away as quickly as he dared. But when he went back round the corner of the Maltings, the sea-man was already waiting for him there. Jack could scarcely breathe. 'Excuse me!' he said loudly, much more loudly than he meant to. And then he did run.

Jack ran up the slip road and right back home. But at his own gate the sea-man was waiting for him. And he nodded – a sort of no-nonsense, come-here, do-this, follow-me nod that Jack suddenly remembered and recognized.

Then the man strode straight to the garden shed. He pointed to the darkest corner, and Jack began to turn over the flower pots, rusty tins, coils of rope and string.

Then Jack saw three gold coins, three shiners in the gloom.

'Dad!' cried Jack. 'Oh, Dad!' And he reached out…

First his father smiled that smile-round-the corner of his. Then he began to fade, fade… He faded and Jack's eyes stung with hot tears.

✏ FILL IN THE GAP

Read the sentences and choose the correct word to fill in each gap.

1 On Saturday morning, Jack went down to the _____.

2 That's where the little fishing-boats tied up and unloaded their _____ and flip-flapping shiners.

3 Jack's father had been the last _____ in those parts, but now he was drowned and food for fishes.

4 He had strings of _____ and pieces of scruff and straw tangled up in his beard and hair.

5 And he was wearing thigh _____ and an old jersey the sea had starched and decorated with wavy patterns.

6 They were white and bloated – like overcooked _____.

7 But when he went back round the corner of the _____, the sea-man was already waiting for him there.

8 But at his own _____ the sea-man was waiting for him.

9 And he nodded – a sort of no-nonsense, come-here, do-this, follow-me nod that Jack suddenly _____ and recognized.

10 Then the man strode straight to the garden _____.

11 Then he began to _____, fade…

12 He faded and Jack's eyes stung with hot _____.

❓ FIVE Ws AND HOW

Answer the questions below. Look back at *Home from the Sea* to find the correct answers.

1 When does Jack go down to the creek?

_____

2 What does Jack go to the creek to do?

_____

3 What does Jack's mum tell him to keep away from?

_____

4 What two things is Jack's mum worried about?

_____

5 What is the man sitting on the end of?

_____

6 What unloads lobsters and flip-flapping shiners?

_____

7 Who used to be a fisherman?

_____

8 What three things are tangled in the man's hair?

_____

9 What two things does Jack grip?

_____

10 Who is already waiting for Jack as he ran around the corner of the Maltings?

_____

11 What does Jack see in the gloom?

_____

12 Who is the sea-man?

_____

◎ MULTIPLE CHOICE

Circle the correct answer to the following questions.

1 What is Jack going to the creek to do?

| hunting | fishing | crabbing | potting |

2 What did Jack want to nose around in?

| Maltings | the river | the jetty | flotsam and jetsam |

3 Who tells Jack to keep away from the edge?

| Dad | sea-man | Mum | fisherman |

4 What was the first thing Jack says to the sea-man?

| 'Hi there' | 'Morning!' | 'Who are you?' | 'Hello' |

5 What sort of patterns are on the sea-man's old jersey?

| spiral | circular | lined | wavy |

6 Where does the sea-man stride towards?

| the garden shed | the house | the garage | the jetty |

7 What does Jack find under the pots and tins?

| a key | a map | jewels | gold coins |

8 What happens to Jack's dad at the end?

| fades away | disappears in a flash | turns dark | becomes brighter |

 **6 HOME FROM THE SEA**

 **TRUE OR FALSE**

Read the sentences. Put a tick in the correct box to show which sentences are true and which are false.

1 Jack was going crabbing with his mum. True ☐ False ☐

2 Jack was going fishing. True ☐ False ☐

3 Jack's family have plenty of food and money. True ☐ False ☐

4 Jack sees a man sat on the jetty. True ☐ False ☐

5 Fishing-boats are unloading lobsters and fish while Jack is there. True ☐ False ☐

6 Jack's dad used to be a fisherman. True ☐ False ☐

7 Jack's dad had drowned. True ☐ False ☐

8 Jack has a long conversation with the sea-man. True ☐ False ☐

9 The sea-man is wearing thigh boots. True ☐ False ☐

10 The sea-man's hands are bloated. True ☐ False ☐

11 The sea-man follows Jack to school. True ☐ False ☐

12 Jack recognises the sea-man's nod. True ☐ False ☐

13 Jack finds gold coins in a chest. True ☐ False ☐

14 The sea-man is Jack's father. True ☐ False ☐

15 The sea-man stays with Jack. True ☐ False ☐

SUMMARISE DRAW AND LABEL

SUMMARISE

1 **Look at the section beginning 'When he rounded…' until 'food for fishes.'. Tick the statement which best summarises this section.**

Jack's mum has lots to worry about. ☐

Jack sees a man on the jetty where the fishermen used to unload their catch. ☐

Jack spots his father and begins to cry. ☐

Jack runs away from the jetty. ☐

2 **Look at the paragraph beginning 'Jack ran up the slip road…'. Write one sentence to summarise what's happening in this paragraph.**

_____

_____

DRAW AND LABEL

Draw the statements in the boxes. Add your own labels to your drawings.

fish being unloaded from fishing boats	the sea-man sitting on the edge of the jetty

123 SEQUENCING

1 **Look at the sentences below. Write the numbers 1 to 4 to show the order the words occur in the sentences.**

Jack gripped his crabbing-stick and pail, and took half-a-step backwards. Then he took another. And then he turned and walked away as quickly as he dared.

backwards	turned	dared	stick

2 **Look at the paragraph beginning "Morning!' Jack said again.'. Number the sentences from 1 to 5 to show the order they occur in the text.**

Jack looked at the man's face and hands. ☐

They were white and bloated – like overcooked potatoes. ☐

In fact, they looked as if they'd burst if you poked them. ☐

'Morning!' Jack said again. ☐

Then the man did look up. ☐

3 **Look at *Home from the Sea*. Number the sentences from 1 to 5 to show the order they occur in the whole text. Look at the first line of each paragraph to help you.**

'You keep away from the edge!' said his mum. ☐

On Saturday morning, Jack went down to the creek. ☐

Jack ran up the slip road and right back home. ☐

First his father smiled that smile-round-the corner of his. ☐

But the man did not reply. ☐

FIND AND COPY

These questions are about *Home from the Sea*.

1 Look at the first paragraph. Find and copy a word that means going fishing for crabs.

_____

2 Look at the paragraph beginning 'When he rounded…'. Find and copy a word that tells us that fish and lobsters are taken off the boats.

_____

3 Look at the paragraph beginning "Morning!' Jack said again'. Find and copy a word that shows that things are stuck in the sea-man's beard.

_____

4 Look at the paragraph beginning 'Jack gripped his crabbing-stick…'. Find and copy a word that tells us that Jack walks as quickly as he has the courage to do.

_____

5 Look at the paragraph beginning 'Jack ran up the slip road…'. Find and copy a word that tells us that Jack realises he had seen these actions before.

_____

6 Look at the paragraph beginning 'Then the man strode…'. Find and copy a word that tells us that the man walked quickly.

_____

Comprehension Ninja 7-8 © Andrew Jennings, 2021

✏ CIRCLE A WORD

Read the paragraphs below and then follow the instructions.

'Morning!' Jack said again. Then the man did look up. He had strings of seaweed and pieces of scruff and straw tangled up in his beard and hair. And he was wearing thigh boots and an old jersey the sea had starched and decorated with wavy patterns. Jack looked at the man's face and hands. They were white and bloated – like overcooked potatoes. In fact, they looked as if they'd burst if you poked them.

Jack gripped his crabbing-stick and pail, and took half-a-step backwards. Then he took another. And then he turned and walked away as quickly as he dared. But when he went back round the corner of the Maltings, the sea-man was already waiting for him there. Jack could scarcely breathe. 'Excuse me!' he said loudly, much more loudly than he meant to. And then he did run.

1 Circle a word that means fabric that is stiff and hardened.

2 Circle a word that tells us that something has things added to it to make it look nice.

3 Circle a word that means cooked for too long.

4 Circle a word that means a metal bucket.

5 Circle a word that tells us that means someone can only just do something.

Little Red Riding Hood from Revolting Rhymes by Roald Dahl.
Published by Jonathan Cape Ltd and Penguin Books Ltd. © Roald Dahl Story Company Ltd, 1982
Comprehension Ninja 7-8 © Andrew Jennings, 2021

LITTLE RED RIDING HOOD

ROALD DAHL

As soon as Wolf began to feel
That he would like a decent meal,
He went and knocked on Grandma's door.
When Grandma opened it, she saw
The sharp white teeth, the horrid grin,
And Wolfie said, 'May I come in?'
Poor Grandmamma was terrified,
'He's going to eat me up!' she cried.
And she was absolutely right.
He ate her up in one big bite.
But Grandmamma was small and tough,
And Wolfie wailed, 'That's not enough!
I haven't yet begun to feel
That I have had a decent meal!'
He ran around the kitchen yelping,
'I've *got* to have a second helping!'
Then added with a frightful leer,
'I'm therefore going to wait right here
Till Little Miss Red Riding Hood
 Comes home from walking in the wood.'
He quickly put on Grandma's clothes.
(Of course he hadn't eaten those.)

Little Red Riding Hood from Revolting Rhymes by Roald Dahl.
Published by Jonathan Cape Ltd and Penguin Books Ltd. © Roald Dahl Story Company Ltd, 1982
Comprehension Ninja 7-8 © Andrew Jennings, 2021

He dressed himself in coat and hat.
He put on shoes and after that
He even brushed and curled his hair,
Then sat himself in Grandma's chair.
In came the little girl in red.
She stopped. She stared. And then she said,
'What great big ears you have, Grandma.'
'All the better to hear you with,' the Wolf replied.
'What great big eyes you have, Grandma,' said Little Red Riding Hood.
'All the better to see you with,' the Wolf replied.
He sat there watching her and smiled.
He thought, I'm going to eat this child.
Compared with her old Grandmamma
She's going to taste like caviare.

Then Little Red Riding Hood said,
'But Grandma, what a lovely great big furry coat you have on.'

'That's wrong!' cried Wolf. 'Have you forgot
To tell me what BIG TEETH I've got?
Ah well, no matter what you say,
I'm going to eat you anyway.'
The small girl smiles. One eyelid flickers.
She whips a pistol from her knickers.
She aims it at the creature's head
And *bang bang bang*, she shoots him dead.
A few weeks later, in the wood,
I came across Miss Riding Hood.
But what a change! No cloak of red,
No silly hood upon her head.
She said, 'Hello, and do please note
My lovely furry WOLFSKIN COAT.'

✏ FILL IN THE GAP

Read the sentences and choose the correct word to fill in each gap.

1 As soon as Wolf began to feel

That he would like a decent _____,

2 He went and _____ on Grandma's door.

When Grandma opened it, she saw

3 Then added with a frightful _____,

'I'm therefore going to wait right here

4 He even brushed and _____ his hair,

Then sat himself in Grandma's chair.

5 He sat there watching her and _____.

He thought, I'm going to eat this child.

6 Compared with her old Grandmamma

She's going to taste like _____.

7 'That's wrong!' cried Wolf. 'Have you _____

'To tell me what BIG TEETH I've got?

8 Ah well, no _____ what you say,

I'm going to eat you anyway.'

9 The small girl smiles. One eyelid flickers.

She whips a pistol from her _____.

10 She aims it at the _____ head

And *bang bang bang*, she shoots him dead.

11 But what a change! No cloak of red,

No silly _____ upon her head.

12 She said, 'Hello, and do please note

My lovely furry _____ COAT.'

    Comprehension Ninja 7-8 © Andrew Jennings, 2021

❓ FIVE Ws AND HOW

Answer the questions below. Look back at *Little Red Riding Hood* to find the correct answers.

1 What does Wolf feel like he needed?

_____

2 Whose door does Wolf knock on?

_____

3 How does Grandma feel about Wolf turning up at her house?

_____

4 How many bites does it take Wolf to eat Grandma?

_____

5 Who does Wolf decide to wait for after eating Grandma?

_____

6 What does Wolf dress himself in?

_____

7 Where does Wolf sit?

_____

8 What does Wolf think Little Red would taste like compared to Grandma?

_____

9 What does Little Red Riding Hood say that Wolf is wearing?

_____

10 What does Little Red Riding Hood whip from her knickers?

_____

11 Where does Little Red Riding Hood aim?

_____

12 What does Little Red Riding Hood change her red cloak to?

_____

◎ MULTIPLE CHOICE

Circle the correct answer to the following questions.

1 When Grandma opened the door, what part of Wolf does she see?

| his long tail | his thick fur | his yellow eyes | his horrid grin |

2 What is the first thing that Wolf said to Grandma?

| 'Hello, Grannie' | 'May I come in?' | 'Hello, Grandmamma' | 'Good afternoon' |

3 How many bites does Wolf take to eat up Grandma?

| one | two | three | four |

4 After eating Grandma, where does Wolf run around?

| the bedroom | the dining room | the living room | the kitchen |

5 What doesn't Wolf eat?

| Grandma's hair | Grandma's nails | Grandma's feet | Grandma's clothes |

6 What does Wolf think Little Red Riding Hood will taste like?

| steak | caviare | lobster | sausages |

7 Where does Little Red Riding Hood pull the pistol from?

| her dress | her knickers | her trousers | her cloak |

8 Which part of Wolf does Little Red Riding Hood aim at?

| his head | his shoulder | his chest | his legs |

 Comprehension Ninja 7-8 © Andrew Jennings, 2021

👎 TRUE OR FALSE

Read the sentences. Put a tick in the correct box to show which sentences are true and which are false.

1 Wolf tried to eat Little Red Riding Hood first.   True ☐   False ☐

2 Wolf ate Grandma up in three big bites.   True ☐   False ☐

3 Grandma was small and tough.   True ☐   False ☐

4 Wolf felt full after eating Grandma.   True ☐   False ☐

5 Wolf ran around the living room.   True ☐   False ☐

6 Wolf straightened his hair with a brush.   True ☐   False ☐

7 Wolf stole Little Red Riding Hood's cloak.   True ☐   False ☐

8 Little Red Riding Hood came from the woods.   True ☐   False ☐

9 Wolf thought Grandma would taste like caviare.   True ☐   False ☐

10 Both of Little Red Riding Hood's eyelids flickered.   True ☐   False ☐

11 Little Red Riding Hood pulled a pistol from her bag.   True ☐   False ☐

12 Little Red Riding Hood fired a single shot at Wolf.   True ☐   False ☐

13 The speaker saw Little Red Riding Hood a few days later.   True ☐   False ☐

14 Little Red Riding Hood looked very different.   True ☐   False ☐

15 Little Red Riding Hood had swapped her red cloak for a furry wolfskin coat.   True ☐   False ☐

SUMMARISE

1 **Look at the section beginning 'Then Little Red Riding Hood said,…' until the end of the poem. Tick the statement which best summarises this section.**

Little Red Riding Hood compliments the wolf's coat. ☐

Little Red Riding Hood talks to the wolf about eating Grandma. ☐

Little Red Riding Hood turns the wolf into the coat. ☐

Little Red Riding Hood shoots the wolf and turns him into a coat. ☐

2 **Read the poem from the beginning up to 'She's going to taste like caviare.'. Write one sentence to summarise what's happening in this section.**

_____

_____

DRAW AND LABEL

Draw the statements in the boxes. Add your own labels to your drawings.

the wolf dressed in Grandma's clothes, hat and shoes	Little Red Riding Hood wearing her new wolfskin coat.

 Comprehension Ninja 7-8 © Andrew Jennings, 2021

123 SEQUENCING

1 **Look at the sentences below. Write the numbers 1 to 4 to show the order the words occur in the sentences.**

But what a change! No cloak of red,
No silly hood upon her head.
She said, 'Hello, and do please note
My lovely furry WOLFSKIN COAT.'

coat	hood	red	note

2 **Look at the section from 'Till Little Miss Red Riding Hood' to '…in Grandma's chair'. Number the lines from 1 to 5 to show the order they occur in the poem.**

He dressed himself in coat and hat. ☐

Then sat himself in Grandma's chair. ☐

Comes home from walking in the wood.' ☐

He quickly put on Grandma's clothes. ☐

(Of course he hadn't eaten those.) ☐

3 **Look at *Little Red Riding Hood*. Number the lines from 1 to 5 to show the order they occur in the whole poem.**

Then sat himself in Grandma's chair. ☐

But Grandmamma was small and tough, ☐

'I'm therefore going to wait right here ☐

But what a change! No cloak of red, ☐

He went and knocked on Grandma's door. ☐

 FIND AND COPY

These questions are about *Little Red Riding Hood*.

1 Look at the whole poem. Find and copy a word that tells us that Wolf scared Grandma.

_____

2 Look at the whole poem. Find and copy a word that shows that Wolf gave an unpleasant look.

_____

3 Look at the whole poem. Find and copy a word that tells us that Little Red Riding Hood's eyelid moves a tiny amount.

_____

4 Look at the whole poem. Find and copy a word that tells us that Little Red Riding Hood takes the pistol out quickly.

_____

5 Look at the whole poem. Find and copy a word that tells us that Little Red Riding Hood points the pistol at Wolf's head.

_____

6 Look at the whole poem. Find and copy a word that tells us that Little Red Riding Hood had a coat made from the wolf's fur.

_____

✏ CIRCLE A WORD

Read the lines below and then follow the instructions.

As soon as Wolf began to feel
That he would like a decent meal,
He went and knocked on Grandma's door.
When Grandma opened it, she saw
The sharp white teeth, the horrid grin,
And Wolfie said, 'May I come in?'
Poor Grandmamma was terrified,
'He's going to eat me up!' she cried.
And she was absolutely right.
He ate her up in one big bite.
But Grandmamma was small and tough,
And Wolfie wailed, 'That's not enough!

1 Circle a word that means enough or sufficient.

2 Circle a word that means to hit a surface to get someone's attention.

3 Circle a word that means unpleasant.

4 Circle a word that means difficult to chew.

5 Circle a word that means spoke in a complaining, moaning way.

THE GOLDEN LIONS

ANDREW JENNINGS

They say that football is the world's most beautiful game,
Sometimes only played for the money or the fame.
But away from all the riches and away from all the glory,
You're sure to find a different game and a very different story.

A story unsurpassed by the World Cups or Premierships,
The story of the love of the game and footballing friendships.
Training in the rain and mud or on the slickest astroturf,
The Golden Lions gave their all, determined to show their worth.

Like something from a dream, wearing navy and gold,
In reality, they were a team, something special to behold.
The Lions' biggest fans: siblings, mums and dads,
Celebrated every moment, no one ever went home sad.

In between the posts, super Ezra was the keeper,
He was brave and nimble and he also played as sweeper.
Thrilling saves he could perform, oh how the supporters cheered,
No matter how great the shot, around the post it would be steered.

Ezra's sister was Ellie, a football legend with all the tricks,
No one ever matched her skills with headers, throws or flicks.
Astounding moves she would perform to dazzle the opposition,
Always playing the perfect pass in the just right position.

Finley was the defensive rock with the heart of a majestic beast,
Strikers could not get past him; his passion was unleashed.
The managers had a secret weapon that no one could ignore,
They'd tactically relocate him with no doubt that he would score.

Rima was the relentless winger, raging up and down the right,
To those who didn't know better, she was like a bird in flight.
Tricky feet and close control, moving around the pitch like lightning,
Smashing balls in the top corner with accuracy that's frightening.

Junior was the football tyrant who loved to hunt and tackle,
Tracking down the helpless ball like a cruel, tenacious jackal.
Up and down, he never stopped: a football manager's dream,
With the engine of a racing car, he'd never run out of steam.

Charlie was the captain, the fearless leader of the pack,
Dribbling forwards with the ball, not once would he look back.
Stunning goals, awesome tackles, playing that perfect pass,
Roaring loud and chasing down over every blade of grass.

Sun, rain or snow, no one worried about the weather,
Win, lose or draw, the lions were always together.
When all was said and done and the final whistle blew,
Whatever the result, it was the best that they could do.

✏ FILL IN THE GAP

Read the sentences and choose the correct word to fill in each gap.

1 The story of the _____ of the game and footballing friendships.

2 Training in the rain and mud or on the _____ astroturf,

3 The Golden Lions gave their all, _____ to show their worth.

4 Like something from a dream, _____ navy and gold,

5 He was brave and _____ and he also played as sweeper.

6 Thrilling saves he could _____, oh how the supporters cheered,

7 No matter how great the shot, around the post it would be _____.

8 Finley was the _____ rock with the heart of a majestic beast,

9 Rima was the _____ winger, raging up and down the right,

10 Smashing balls in the top corner with _____ that's frightening.

11 Tracking down the helpless ball like a _____, tenacious jackal.

12 Sun, _____ or snow, no one worried about the weather,

? FIVE Ws AND HOW

Answer the questions below. Look back at *The Golden Lions* to find the correct answers.

1 Who are the Golden Lions' biggest fans?

_____

2 Who is the goalkeeper?

_____

3 Who is brave and nimble?

_____

4 Who is the legend with all the tricks?

_____

5 Who performs astounding moves?

_____

6 Who has the heart of a majestic beast?

_____

7 Who would score no matter where he plays?

_____

8 Who is the relentless winger?

_____

9 Who smashes balls into the top corner?

_____

10 Who is the football tyrant?

_____

11 Who is a football manager's dream?

_____

12 Who is the captain?

_____

◎ MULTIPLE CHOICE

Circle the correct answer to the following questions.

1 As well as in the rain or mud, where else do the Golden Lions train?

| sports hall | astroturf | tarmac | grass |

2 What colours do the Golden Lions wear?

| red and black | white and yellow | navy and gold | green and silver |

3 Who cheers when Ezra performs saves?

| mum and dad | siblings | other players | supporters |

4 Ezra is the keeper, but what other position could he play?

| striker | defender | winger | sweeper |

5 Who is the football legend with all the tricks?

| Ellie | Ezra | Charlie | Finley |

6 Who can move like a bird in flight?

| Junior | Rima | Ezra | Charlie |

7 What does Junior love to do?

| score and tackle | hunt and tackle | hunt and dribble | score and dribble |

8 Who is the fearless leader of the pack?

| Finley | Rima | Ellie | Charlie |

Comprehension Ninja 7-8 © Andrew Jennings, 2021

 **TRUE OR FALSE**

Read the sentences. Put a tick in the correct box to show which sentences are true and which are false.

1	The Golden Lions sometimes train in the rain and mud.	True ☐	False ☐
2	The Golden Lions give their all.	True ☐	False ☐
3	The Golden Lions are determined to show their worth.	True ☐	False ☐
4	The Golden Lions wear yellow and green.	True ☐	False ☐
5	Sometimes the Lions' fans go home sad.	True ☐	False ☐
6	Ezra performs dazzling tricks.	True ☐	False ☐
7	Ellie is the Golden Lions' biggest fan.	True ☐	False ☐
8	Finley is the manager's secret weapon.	True ☐	False ☐
9	Finley is found in between the posts.	True ☐	False ☐
10	Rima can score with accuracy.	True ☐	False ☐
11	Junior moves around the pitch like lightning.	True ☐	False ☐
12	Junior never stops during a game.	True ☐	False ☐
13	Charlie is the captain of the team.	True ☐	False ☐
14	Charlie covers every blade of grass.	True ☐	False ☐
15	The Golden Lions always do the best they could.	True ☐	False ☐

✏ SUMMARISE ✏ DRAW AND LABEL

SUMMARISE

1 **Look at the verse beginning 'Finley was the…'. Tick the statement which best summarises this verse.**

Finley is a defender who could also play as a goal scorer. ☐

Finley is a defender who had hair like a lion. ☐

Finley is the team's secret weapon. ☐

Finley is the manager's favourite player. ☐

2 **Look at the verse beginning 'Junior was the football tyrant…'. Write one sentence to summarise what's happening in this verse.**

_____

_____

DRAW AND LABEL

Draw the statements in the boxes. Add your own labels to your drawings.

Ezra could perform thrilling saves	Rima smashing balls in the top corner

Comprehension Ninja 7-8 © Andrew Jennings, 2021

123 SEQUENCING

1 **Look at the lines below. Write the numbers 1 to 4 to show the order the words occur in the lines.**

Sun, rain or snow, no one worried about the weather,
Win, lose or draw, the lions were always together.

together	snow	draw	weather

2 **Look at the lines from 'Junior was the football tyrant…' to 'run out of steam'. Number the lines from 1 to 5 to show the order they occur in the poem.**

like a cruel, tenacious jackal.

Up and down, he never stopped

Tracking down the helpless ball

a football manager's dream,

he'd never run out of steam.

3 **Look at *The Golden Lions*. Number the lines from 1 to 5 to show the order they occur in the whole poem. Look at the first line of each verse to help you.**

A story unsurpassed by the World Cups or Premierships,

They say that football is the world's most beautiful game,

Charlie was the captain, the fearless leader of the pack,

In between the posts, super Ezra was the keeper

Sun, rain or snow, no one worried about the weather,

👀 FIND AND COPY

These questions are about *The Golden Lions*.

1   Look at the verse beginning 'Like something from a dream…'. Find and copy a word that tells us that the kit was blue.

_____

2   Look at the verse beginning 'Ezra's sister was Ellie…'. Find and copy a word that shows that Ellie's skills would blind the opposition for a moment.

_____

3   Look at the verse beginning 'Finley was…'. Find and copy a word that tells us that the managers would move Finley.

_____

4   Look at the verse beginning 'Rima was…'. Find and copy a word that shows that Rima never stopped running up and down the side of the pitch.

_____

5   Look at the verse beginning 'Junior was…'. Find and copy a word that tells us that the ball couldn't defend itself or hide from Junior.

_____

6   Look at the verse beginning 'Charlie was…'. Find and copy a word that shows that Charlie was often shouting.

_____

CIRCLE A WORD

Read the verses below and then follow the instructions.

> They say that football is the world's most beautiful game,
> Sometimes only played for the money or the fame.
> But away from all the riches and away from all the glory,
> You're sure to find a different game and a very different story.
>
> A story unsurpassed by the World Cups or Premierships,
> The story of the love of the game and footballing friendships.
> Training in the rain and mud or on the slickest astroturf,
> The Golden Lions gave their all, determined to show their worth.

1 Circle a word that means known by many people.

2 Circle a word that tells us that something is better or greater than any other.

3 Circle a word that means emotional relationships between people.

4 Circle a word that means practising a sport.

5 Circle a word that means value.

KNIGHTS AND BIKES

GABRIELLE KENT

The creature wriggled away from her and struggled to its feet before flinging off the blanket and putting its hands up in the air. A large duffel bag containing something big and rectangular fell to the floor.

'I said, OK, I surrender!' said the demon, which Demelza had to admit was starting to look much less like hell-spawn, and more like a girl not much older than her.

She had brown skin and punky black hair. Her leather gloves were fingerless and she was wearing slouchy leather ankle boots and not one but TWO earrings in one ear. She was the coolest-looking burglar Demelza had ever seen. She was also the *first* burglar Demelza had ever seen.

The girl bent down to pick up her duffel bag and Demelza pointed her battered sword warily at her.

'You're not from here,' she said, narrowing her eyes. 'I know everyone on Penfurzy Island, and you're not anyone I know.'

'Just passing through,' said the girl, brushing the tip of the sword away, then rolling up her sleeve to rub at the little red peck marks Captain Honkers had left on her arm. 'I thought this place was empty. I'm not sticking around – I was just after somewhere to sleep tonight. Sorry I scared you. I'll be off now, OK?'

'Scared?' said Demelza, her frizzy red bunches bouncing as she leapt to block the girl's path to the door. 'We weren't scared, was we, Honkers?' She grabbed the goose and held him under one arm.

'Honk!' said Captain Honkers.

'Sure. OK, kid, you weren't scared. Now, if you'll move, I'll go and find somewhere else for the night.'

Demelza stood firm. 'Who you calling kid? What are you? Ten or eleven? You's just a kid too. So, shut up, stupid-head!'

'Say it, don't spray it,' said the girl, wiping her face with the back of her hand in an exaggerated motion.

'So, are you going to get out of my way? Or are you going to try to stab me to death with your toy sword?'

Demelza scratched her chin, accidentally picking the top off a scab she had forgotten was there. 'I haven't decided yet,' she said. 'If I do let you out, where'll you go?'

The girl shrugged as she slung her bag over her shoulder. 'What's it to you, short stuff?'

The wind whistled around the caravan, blowing open the door and driving the icy rain forcefully against the windows. Demelza could see goose pimples all over the girl's arms. Her hair and jeans were also dripping wet and she was only wearing a T-shirt under her light denim jacket.

Demelza chewed her lip. Even though this very strange stranger had invaded their fortress, suggested that she was scared, AND called her short, she wouldn't send even her worst enemy out near the cliffs on a stormy night like this.

✏ FILL IN THE GAP

Read the sentences and choose the correct word to fill in each gap.

1 The creature _____ away from her and struggled to its feet before flinging off the blanket and putting its hands up in the air.

2 'I said, OK, I surrender!' said the _____, which Demelza had to admit was starting to look much less like hell-spawn, and more like a girl not much older than her.

3 Her leather gloves were _____ and she was wearing slouchy leather ankle boots and not one but TWO earrings in one ear.

4 The girl bent down to pick up her duffel bag and Demelza pointed her _____ sword warily at her.

5 'Just passing through,' said the girl, brushing the tip of the sword away, then rolling up her sleeve to rub at the little red peck marks Captain _____ had left on her arm.

6 'Scared?' said Demelza, her frizzy red _____ bouncing as she leapt to block the girl's path to the door.

7 'Say it, don't _____ it,' said the girl, wiping her face with the back of her hand in an exaggerated motion.

8 'Or are you going to try to stab me to death with your _____ sword?'

9 Demelza scratched her _____, accidentally picking the top off a scab she had forgotten was there.

10 The wind whistled around the _____, blowing open the door and driving the icy rain forcefully against the windows.

11 Demelza could see goose pimples all over the girl's _____.

12 Even though this very strange stranger had invaded their fortress, suggested that she was scared, AND called her short, she wouldn't send even her worst _____ out near the cliffs on a stormy night like this.

? FIVE Ws AND HOW

Answer the questions below. Look back at *Knights and Bikes* to find the correct answers.

1 What contains something big and rectangular?

_____

2 What does the demon creature turn out to be?

_____

3 How many earrings does the girl have in one ear?

_____

4 What island does Demelza live on?

_____

5 What does Demelza point at the girl?

_____

6 Who leaves red peck marks on the girl's arm?

_____

7 What does the unknown girl want?

_____

8 What colour is Demelza's hair?

_____

9 What kind of animal is Captain Honkers?

_____

10 What type of accommodation are the girls inside?

_____

11 Where can Demelza see goose pimples on the girl?

_____

12 What material is the unknown girl's jacket made of?

_____

Comprehension Ninja 7-8 © Andrew Jennings, 2021

◎ MULTIPLE CHOICE

Circle the correct answer to the following questions.

1 How many earrings does the girl have in one of her ears?

| one | two | three | four |

2 The girl was the first what, that Demelza had ever seen?

| ghost | pirate | burglar | demon |

3 What does Demelza point at the unknown girl?

| a spear | a metal post | a sword | a crossbow |

4 On which island does Demelza know everyone?

| Penfury | Penfurzy | Penfursy | Penfully |

5 What is the name of the goose?

| Captain Demelza | Captain Caravan | Captain Zonkers | Captain Honkers |

6 What kind of hair does Demelza have?

| punky black hair | frizzy red bunches | golden straight hair | deep brown curls |

7 Where does Demelza hold the goose?

| on her shoulder | in a bag | under one arm | inside her jacket |

8 What can Demelza see on the girl's arms?

| scars | scabs | goose pimples | fur |

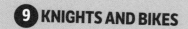

TRUE OR FALSE

Read the sentences. Put a tick in the correct box to show which sentences are true and which are false.

1	The creature in the blanket was a demon.	True ☐	False ☐
2	The girl who was hiding is called Demelza.	True ☐	False ☐
3	Demelza has punky black hair.	True ☐	False ☐
4	Demelza points a sword at the unknown girl.	True ☐	False ☐
5	Demelza knows everyone from Penfurzy Island.	True ☐	False ☐
6	The unknown girl thought the caravan was empty.	True ☐	False ☐
7	Demelza has frizzy red bunches.	True ☐	False ☐
8	Demelza blocks the girl's path to leave the caravan.	True ☐	False ☐
9	Captain Honkers is a goose.	True ☐	False ☐
10	Demelza accidentally knocks a scab off her elbow.	True ☐	False ☐
11	The unknown girl calls Demelza "tall stuff".	True ☐	False ☐
12	The girls are in a caravan.	True ☐	False ☐
13	The sun is shining outside the caravan.	True ☐	False ☐
14	Goose pimples are all over the girl's arm.	True ☐	False ☐
15	Demelza is worried about someone being near the cliffs on a stormy night.	True ☐	False ☐

✏ SUMMARISE 🏷 DRAW AND LABEL

SUMMARISE

1 **Look at the section from 'The wind whistled…' until the end of the text. Tick the statement which best summarises this section.**

Even though the weather was terrible, she didn't want the stranger to stay. ☐

Demelza didn't want to help the stranger. ☐

Demelza didn't want to be cold anymore in the caravan. ☐

Demelza didn't want to send the stranger away into the terrible weather. ☐

2 **Look at the first paragraph. Write one sentence to summarise what's happening in this paragraph.**

_____

_____

DRAW AND LABEL

Draw the statements in the boxes. Add your own labels to your drawings.

a caravan in a storm	Demelza pointing a sword at the unknown girl

1 **Look at the sentences below. Write the numbers 1 to 4 to show the order the words occur in the sentences.**

The creature wriggled away from her and struggled to its feet before flinging off the blanket and putting its hands up in the air. A large duffel bag containing something big and rectangular fell to the floor.

flinging	wriggled	duffel	rectangular

2 **Look at the paragraph beginning with 'The girl shrugged…' until the end of the text. Number the sentences from 1 to 5 to show the order they occur in the text.**

'What's it to you, short stuff?'

Her hair and jeans were also dripping wet and she was only wearing a T-shirt under her light denim jacket.

Demelza chewed her lip.

The wind whistled around the caravan, blowing open the door and driving the icy rain forcefully against the windows.

Demelza could see goose pimples all over the girl's arms.

3 **Look at *Knights and Bikes*. Number the sentences from 1 to 5 to show the order they occur in the whole text. Look at the first line of each paragraph to help you.**

Demelza chewed her lip.

'Honk!' said Captain Honkers.

She had brown skin and punky black hair.

The girl shrugged as she slung her bag over her shoulder.

'So, are you going to get out of my way?'

👁️ FIND AND COPY

These questions are about *Knights and Bikes*.

1 Look at the first paragraph. Find and copy a word that shows that the unknown girl found it hard to stand up.

_____

2 Look at the paragraph beginning 'She had brown skin…'. Find and copy a word that tells us that Demelza thought the girl was there to steal her things.

_____

3 Look at the paragraph beginning 'Just passing through…'. Find and copy a word that tells us that the goose had nipped the girl with his beak.

_____

4 Look at the paragraph beginning 'The wind…'. Find and copy a word that tells us that the wind made a high-pitched noise.

_____

5 Look at the paragraph beginning 'The wind…'. Find and copy a word that tells us that the rain was cold.

_____

6 Look at the last paragraph. Find and copy a word that tells us that the stranger had suggested that Demelza was frightened.

_____

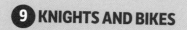

CIRCLE A WORD

Read the paragraphs below and then follow the instructions.

The creature wriggled away from her and struggled to its feet before flinging off the blanket and putting its hands up in the air. A large duffel bag containing something big and rectangular fell to the floor.

'I said, OK, I surrender!' said the demon, which Demelza had to admit was starting to look much less like hell-spawn, and more like a girl not much older than her.

She had brown skin and punky black hair. Her leather gloves were fingerless and she was wearing slouchy leather ankle boots and not one but TWO earrings in one ear. She was the coolest-looking burglar Demelza had ever seen. She was also the first *burglar* Demelza had ever seen.

1 Circle a word that means twisted and turned on the floor.

2 Circle a word that means shaped like a rectangle.

3 Circle a word that means to give up or submit.

4 Circle a word that tells us that her boots were loose or not tightly fitting.

5 Circle a word that means someone who steals things from others.

GRANNY TING TING

PATRICE LAWRENCE

It was Saturday morning. Shayla was helping Mommy fold sheets. A deep, trumpeting noise came from outside. Shayla ran out and spotted Michael high in the branches of the lime tree with Granny's conch shell to his lips.

After a quick check for scary caterpillars, she climbed up to join him. They sat side by side on the branch, watching the world below.

"What's it like, living in London?" Shayla said. "You seem to think it's much better than Arouca."

"London's brilliant. You're never bored. You can go on boat trips on the river. And there's this massive wheel that's taller than a building and you sit in a pod and look across the whole of the city. There's a zoo –"

"Trinidad's got a zoo."

"London's is bigger. And in winter you can go ice-skating outside."

"You can't do that in Trinidad," Shayla said. "But we *do* have the beach. Mommy's going to take us there and we're leaving in an hour!"

FICTION: EXTRACT

The beach was a long drive away. The car wound its way along steep roads where waterfalls trickled down the hillside. Weaver-bird nests hung like old socks from high branches.

Then, at last…

Clear sky. The wrinkly sea. And fun.

The cousins sat at the water's edge. Waves splashed over them. Black cormorants swooped down for fish.

Later, they rummaged around in a river pool. Michael collected tiny black tadpoles.

"Frogpoles!" They hopped up his arm. "Not quite tadpoles or frogs."

Shayla showed him holes in the sand dunes where crabs lived. She told him about the turtles coming out at night to lay their eggs. You had to be very quiet if you wanted to see them.

Just before they went home, Mommy bought them snow cones – flaky ice and red syrup.

"So do you still think London is better than Trinidad?" Shayla asked her cousin as they got back in the car.

"Trinidad does have *some* cool things," Michael admitted.

✏ FILL IN THE GAP

Read the sentences and choose the correct word to fill in each gap.

1 A deep, _____ noise came from outside.

2 Shayla ran out and spotted Michael high in the branches of the _____ tree with Granny's conch shell to his lips.

3 After a quick check for scary _____, she climbed up to join him.

4 And there's this massive _____ that's taller than a building and you sit in a pod and look across the whole of the city.

5 "London's is _____. And in winter you can go ice-skating outside."

6 The car wound its way along steep roads where _____ trickled down the hillside.

7 Black _____ swooped down for fish.

8 Michael collected tiny black _____.

9 She told him about the _____ coming out at night to lay their eggs.

10 Just before they went home, Mommy bought them _____ cones – flaky ice and red syrup.

11 "So do you still think London is better than _____?" Shayla asked her cousin as they got back in the car.

12 "Trinidad does have *some* cool things," Michael _____.

  Comprehension Ninja 7-8 © Andrew Jennings, 2021

❓ FIVE Ws AND HOW

Answer the questions below. Look back at *Granny Ting Ting* to find the correct answers.

1 Who is helping Mommy fold sheets?

_____

2 What two words describe the noise that comes from outside?

_____

3 Who is in the branches of the lime tree?

_____

4 What is Michael using to make the noise?

_____

5 What does Shayla check for, before climbing the tree?

_____

6 Who lives in London?

_____

7 Which place has a bigger zoo?

_____

8 What can you do in winter in London?

_____

9 Where does Shayla's mum take her and Michael?

_____

10 What is trickling down the hillsides?

_____

11 What swoops down for fish?

_____

12 What lives in the holes in the sand dunes?

_____

◎ MULTIPLE CHOICE

Circle the correct answer to the following questions.

1 What sort of tree is Michael sat in?

| lemon | lime | orange | banana |

2 Whose shell did Michael use to make the trumpeting noise?

| Mummy's | Shayla's | Michael's | Granny's |

3 What would you sit in on the large wheel in London?

| a bubble | a pod | a unit | a sphere |

4 Which birds hang nests like old socks from high branches?

| cormorants | hummingbirds | weaver birds | magpies |

5 What does Michael collect?

| turtles | tadpoles | crabs | cormorants |

6 Which animals live in the sand dunes?

| crabs | tortoises | seals | parrots |

7 Which animals lay their eggs at night?

| seals | crabs | turtles | cormorants |

8 What relationship do Michael and Shayla have to each other?

| friends | cousins | siblings | mother and son |

Comprehension Ninja 7-8 © Andrew Jennings, 2021

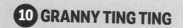 TRUE OR FALSE

Read the sentences. Put a tick in the correct box to show which sentences are true and which are false.

1 Michael lives in London. True ☐ False ☐

2 Michael uses a horn to make a loud noise. True ☐ False ☐

3 Shayla checks the tree for caterpillars. True ☐ False ☐

4 Trinidad's zoo is bigger than London's. True ☐ False ☐

5 Trinidad has a beach. True ☐ False ☐

6 Michael's mum takes Shayla and Michael to the beach. True ☐ False ☐

7 It is a short drive to get to the beach. True ☐ False ☐

8 Black cormorants swoop down for fish. True ☐ False ☐

9 Weaver birds swoop down for fish. True ☐ False ☐

10 Toads hop up Michael's arm. True ☐ False ☐

11 Tortoises hide in caves in the sand dunes. True ☐ False ☐

12 Turtles come out at night to lay their eggs. True ☐ False ☐

13 Shayla's mum bought the children snow cones. True ☐ False ☐

14 The snow cones are covered in lime and coconut. True ☐ False ☐

15 Michael is Shayla's brother. True ☐ False ☐

✏ SUMMARISE ✏ DRAW AND LABEL

SUMMARISE

1 **Look at the last two sentences of the text. Tick the statement which best summarises this section.**

Shayla and Michael went to the beach in the car. ☐

Shayla and Michael explore the river pool and find tadpoles. ☐

Shayla asks Michael if London is better than Trinidad, and he says Trinidad has some cool things. ☐

Shayla and Michael talk about how London is better than Trinidad. ☐

2 **Look at the first paragraph. Write one sentence to summarise what's happening in this paragraph.**

_____

_____

DRAW AND LABEL

Draw the statements in the boxes. Add your own labels to your drawings.

Shayla and Michael watching turtles lay eggs.	Mommy bought the children snow cones – flaky ice and red syrup.

123 SEQUENCING

1 **Look at the sentences below. Write the numbers 1 to 4 to show the order the words occur in the sentences.**

After a quick check for scary caterpillars, she climbed up to join him. They sat side by side on the branch, watching the world below.

join	scary	branch	world

2 **Look at the first two paragraphs. Number the sentences from 1 to 5 to show the order they occur in the text.**

They sat side by side on the branch, watching the world below. ☐

A deep, trumpeting noise came from outside. ☐

It was Saturday morning. ☐

Shayla was helping Mommy fold sheets. ☐

After a quick check for scary caterpillars, she climbed up to join him. ☐

3 **Look at *Granny Ting Ting*. Number the sentences from 1 to 5 to show the order they occur in the whole text. Look at the last line of each paragraph to help you.**

They sat side by side on the branch, watching the world below. ☐

Weaver-bird nests hung like old socks from high branches. ☐

"Trinidad's got a zoo." ☐

"Trinidad does have *some* cool things," Michael admitted. ☐

"Not quite tadpoles or frogs." ☐

FIND AND COPY

These questions are about *Granny Ting Ting*.

1 Look at the first paragraph. Find and copy a word that tells us that Shayla managed to see or notice where Michael was.

_____

2 Look at the second paragraph. Find and copy a word that shows that Shayla was afraid of caterpillars.

_____

3 Look at the paragraph beginning with "'London's brilliant.'". Find and copy a word that tells us that the wheel is very big.

_____

4 Look at the paragraph beginning with 'The beach was…'. Find and copy a word that shows that the road twisted and turned up the hill.

_____

5 Look at the paragraph beginning with 'Shayla showed him…'. Find and copy a word that means not making much noise.

_____

6 Look at the last paragraph. Find and copy a word that means that Michael agreed with Shayla.

_____

✏ CIRCLE A WORD

Read the paragraphs below and then follow the instructions.

The beach was a long drive away. The car wound its way along steep roads where waterfalls trickled down the hillside. Weaver-bird nests hung like old socks from high branches.

Then, at last…

Clear sky. The wrinkly sea. And fun.

The cousins sat at the water's edge. Waves splashed over them. Black cormorants swooped down for fish.

Later, they rummaged around in a river pool. Michael collected tiny black tadpoles

1 Circle a word that means when a liquid is only flowing a bit.

2 Circle a word that means free of cloud, mist or rain.

3 Circle a word that means to move downwards quickly through the air.

4 Circle a word that means searched for something with no plan or order.

5 Circle a word that means gathered together.

The Chocolate Unicorn © Jenny McLachlan 2020. Reproduced with the permission of Bloomsbury Publishing Plc
Comprehension Ninja 7-8 © Andrew Jennings, 2021

THE CHOCOLATE UNICORN

JENNY McLACHLAN

They explored the rock pools and collected shells.

When the chocolate unicorn saw a boy making a sandcastle his eyes grew wide. "I'd *love* to do that," he said. "Let's help!"

"What if he doesn't want us to?" said Olive. "There's only one way to find out," said the chocolate unicorn. "Let's ask him."

So Olive walked over to the boy and said, "Please can we play with you?"

The boy looked up, smiled, then passed her a bucket. His name was Eric (it said so on his t-shirt). He didn't talk to Olive, but they still built an amazing sandcastle together.

Olive was digging the moat, when Mum asked if she wanted to come for a swim.

"Do you want to come in the sea, Eric?" said Olive.

Eric looked at the tumbling waves and screaming children and shook his head. Olive understood. Usually she paddled at the edge of the water, too scared of the noise and the waves to go any further.

But today she felt different. Today, she felt brave.

"Will you come in the sea?" she asked the chocolate unicorn.

"I can't," he said sadly. "It's too wet for me. I'd go gloopy."

He was right. The sea was no place for a chocolate unicorn, but it was just the place for Olive. So she left him with Eric and ran towards the sea.

A big wave got Olive right in the face. It knocked her down and Mum pulled her up again. She screamed as she jumped over waves and as waves jumped over her.

It was so much fun that Olive stayed in the sea until her fingers were wrinkly and she was shivering with cold.

As they walked up the beach, Mum said, "I suppose the chocolate unicorn made you do that?"

"No, it was all me!" laughed Olive.

Chapter Six

Back at the sandcastle, Olive found Eric chatting away to the chocolate unicorn.
He stopped talking as soon as he saw Olive.

"You can play with him if you want," said Olive.

Eric smiled and built the chocolate unicorn a sandy cave to keep him out of the sun.

Together, they made the sandcastle bigger and bigger until Eric's dad said it was time to go home.

As Eric packed up his buckets and spades, Olive said to the chocolate unicorn, "I've been thinking. Would you like to go home with Eric? I think he's shy, but he'd love talking to you."

"That would be fun," said the chocolate unicorn, then he looked sad.

"But I think I will miss you, Olive!"

"I will miss you too," said Olive, "but I will never, ever forget you."

✏ FILL IN THE GAP

Read the sentences and choose the correct word to fill in each gap.

1 When the chocolate unicorn saw a boy making a _____ his eyes grew wide.

2 "What if he doesn't want us to?" said _____ .

3 So Olive _____ over to the boy and said, "Please can we play with you?"

4 The boy looked up, smiled, then _____ her a bucket.

5 Usually she paddled at the _____ of the water, too scared of the noise and the waves to go any further.

6 "It's too wet for me. I'd go _____ ."

7 It _____ her down and Mum pulled her up again.

8 It was so much fun that Olive stayed in the sea until her fingers were _____ and she was shivering with cold.

9 Back at the sandcastle, Olive found Eric _____ away to the chocolate unicorn.

10 _____ , they made the sandcastle bigger and bigger until Eric's dad said it was time to go home.

11 "I've been thinking. Would you like to go _____ with Eric?"

12 "I will _____ you too," said Olive, "but I will never, ever forget you."

❓ FIVE Ws AND HOW

Answer the questions below. Look back at *The Chocolate Unicorn* to find the correct answers.

1 Where is the story set?

_____

2 What is Eric building that makes the chocolate unicorn's eyes grow wide?

_____

3 What is the unicorn made from?

_____

4 Where does Olive see Eric's name?

_____

5 Where does Olive ask Eric if he wants to go to?

_____

6 How is Olive feeling today?

_____

7 Who does Olive go in the sea with?

_____

8 Who does the chocolate unicorn stay with when Olive goes in the sea?

_____

9 What knocks Olive down?

_____

10 What does Eric build the chocolate unicorn to keep him out of the sun?

_____

11 What does Eric pack up when it's time to go home?

_____

12 Who does the chocolate unicorn go home with?

_____

◉ MULTIPLE CHOICE

Circle the correct answer to the following questions.

1 Where do Olive and the chocolate unicorn explore?

| the sand dunes | the beach | the rock pools | the forest |

2 What does Eric pass Olive when she asks to play with him?

| a spade | a shovel | a rake | a bucket |

3 On which piece of clothing does Olive see Eric's name?

| his hat | his t-shirt | his jacket | his shorts |

4 What is Olive digging when her mum asks if she wants to come for a swim?

| a tower | a river | a cave | a moat |

5 How does Olive feel at the beach?

| scared | brave | excited | happy |

6 Who would go gloopy in the sea?

| the chocolate unicorn | Eric | Olive | Mum |

7 Where does a big wave hit Olive?

| her feet | her face | her legs | her hands |

8 What does Eric build for the chocolate unicorn to keep him out of the sun?

| a hole | an umbrella | a hat | a cave |

TRUE OR FALSE

Read the sentences. Put a tick in the correct box to show which sentences are true and which are false.

1	Olive and the chocolate unicorn explore rock pools.	True ☐	False ☐
2	Olive sees a boy making a sandcastle.	True ☐	False ☐
3	Eric's name is on his hat.	True ☐	False ☐
4	Olive digs the moat for the castle.	True ☐	False ☐
5	Eric asks Olive if she wants to go in the sea.	True ☐	False ☐
6	The chocolate unicorn forces Olive to go in the sea.	True ☐	False ☐
7	Olive feels brave today.	True ☐	False ☐
8	The chocolate unicorn goes into the sea too.	True ☐	False ☐
9	Olive gets knocked over by a big wave.	True ☐	False ☐
10	Olive was shivering with cold before she went in the sea.	True ☐	False ☐
11	Eric builds a cave to keep the chocolate unicorn out of the sun.	True ☐	False ☐
12	Olive's mum is the one who tells Olive and Eric it is time to go home.	True ☐	False ☐
13	Olive thinks Eric is shy.	True ☐	False ☐
14	The chocolate unicorn goes home with Olive.	True ☐	False ☐
15	Olive will miss the chocolate unicorn.	True ☐	False ☐

✏ SUMMARISE 🏷 DRAW AND LABEL

SUMMARISE

1 **Read from Chapter Six until the end of the text. Tick the statement which best summarises this section.**

Olive talks to Eric about playing in the sea. ☐

Olive waves goodbye to Eric and his dad. ☐

Olive suggests that the chocolate unicorn goes with Eric. ☐

Olive digs a cave to keep the chocolate unicorn out of the sun. ☐

2 **Look at the paragraph beginning "'Do you want to come in the sea, Eric?'". Write one sentence to summarise what's happening in this paragraph.**

_____

_____

DRAW AND LABEL

Draw the statements in the boxes. Add your own labels to your drawings.

Olive and Eric building a sandcastle	Olive and her mum jumping over waves in the sea

123 SEQUENCING

1 **Look at the sentences below. Write the numbers 1 to 4 to show the order the words occur in the sentences.**

The boy looked up, smiled, then passed her a bucket. His name was Eric (it said so on his t-shirt). He didn't talk to Olive, but they still built an amazing sandcastle together.

bucket	together	talk	t-shirt

2 **Look at the section from 'He was right.' to '...jumped over her.'. Number the sentences from 1 to 5 to show the order they occur in the text.**

So she left him with Eric and ran towards the sea.

A big wave got Olive right in the face.

It knocked her down and Mum pulled her up again.

She screamed as she jumped over waves and as waves jumped over her.

The sea was no place for a chocolate unicorn, but it was just the place for Olive.

3 **Look at *The Chocolate Unicorn*. Number the sentences from 1 to 5 to show the order they occur in the whole text. Look at the first line of each paragraph to help you.**

They explored the rock pools and collected shells.

Olive was digging the moat, when Mum asked if she wanted to come for a swim.

"I will miss you too," said Olive, "but I will never, ever forget you."

But today she felt different.

"You can play with him if you want," said Olive.

FIND AND COPY

These questions are about *The Chocolate Unicorn*.

1 Look at the paragraph beginning 'When the chocolate unicorn…'. Find and copy a word that shows that the chocolate unicorn really wants to make a sandcastle.

_____

2 Look at the paragraph beginning 'The boy looked up…'. Find and copy a word that tells us that Olive and Eric both built the sandcastle.

_____

3 Look at the paragraph beginning 'Eric looked at the tumbling waves…'. Find and copy a word that tells us that the children were making lots of noise.

_____

4 Look at the paragraph beginning 'A big wave got Olive…'. Find and copy a word that tells us that Mum pulled Olive up more than once.

_____

5 Look at the paragraph beginning 'It was so much fun…'. Find and copy a word that tells us that Olive was shaking.

_____

6 Look at the paragraph beginning 'Back at the sandcastle…'. Find and copy a word that tells us that Eric was talking.

_____

CIRCLE A WORD

Read the paragraphs below and then follow the instructions.

Eric smiled and built the chocolate unicorn a sandy cave to keep him out of the sun.

Together, they made the sandcastle bigger and bigger until Eric's dad said it was time to go home.

As Eric packed up his buckets and spades, Olive said to the chocolate unicorn, "I've been thinking. Would you like to go home with Eric? I think he's shy, but he'd love talking to you."

"That would be fun," said the chocolate unicorn, then he looked sad.

"But I think I will miss you, Olive!"

"I will miss you too," said Olive, "but I will never, ever forget you."

1 Circle a word that means a hole in the middle of cliffs.

2 Circle a word that means containers with handles.

3 Circle a word that tells us that a person is quiet and nervous about talking to people.

4 Circle a word that means that someone is sad because someone they like isn't around.

5 Circle a word that means to not remember.

AGENT ZAIBA INVESTIGATES: THE MISSING DIAMONDS

Extract from *Agent Zaiba Investigates: The Missing Diamonds* © Speckled Pen Limited 2020, reproduced by permission of Stripes Publishing Limited
Comprehension Ninja 7-8 © Andrew Jennings, 2021

ANNABELLE SAMI

This party definitely had the three main ingredients for a successful Mehndi party in abundance – food, music and dancing! At the top of the room on a little stage was Sam. As the bride-to-be, she sat on a gilded white lounge chair, wearing a sari in deep red, orange and yellow. Zaiba saw her cousin stifle a yawn as she continued to sit patiently while her hands were decorated with the henna. Meanwhile her fiancé, Tanvir, had been cornered next to the punchbowl by some eager aunties who wanted to know *everything* about the upcoming wedding. It seemed at the moment that this party was fun for everyone *but* the young couple.

Zaiba felt a stab of sadness. Sam was her favourite cousin and Zaiba wanted this evening to be everything she'd hoped it would be. She glanced around the room, taking a mental note of as many details as possible. As the linen curtains swelled in the breeze, she noticed that the patio doors opened *out* on to the garden, rather than *in* to the room. That could be useful information if they were involved in a high-stakes chase! There was a main entrance leading out on to the drive too. She eased a little gold pencil that the receptionist had given her out of her bag and added extra details to the hotel map she'd drawn that morning. The receptionist – "Liza with a 'z'!" – had taken Zaiba and some of the other children round the hotel while their parents were busy unpacking. She'd pointed out the twenty-six bedrooms, the library with its leather-bound books and the extensive hotel grounds and separate buildings.

Zaiba opened the phone's voice recorder again and put it to her lips. "Observations: number of guests one, two, three, four, five… uhhhh, at least fifty people. Sofas and soft seating at ninety degrees to my right. Most people are on the dance floor. Bad – no *really* bad – music from the DJ booth close to the north-east window. No suspicious activity so far–"

"Apart from the girl hiding under the dining table!"

The tablecloth whipped up and a hand reached for Zaiba, pulling her swiftly out from her observation point.

"Aunt Fouzia!" Zaiba groaned, annoyed that she'd been discovered.

✏️ FILL IN THE GAP

Read the sentences and choose the correct word to fill in each gap.

1 This party definitely had the three main ingredients for a _____ Mehndi party in abundance – food, music and dancing!

2 As the _____-to-be, she sat on a gilded white lounge chair, wearing a sari in deep red, orange and yellow.

3 Meanwhile her fiancé, Tanvir, had been cornered next to the _____ by some eager aunties who wanted to know everything about the upcoming wedding.

4 It seemed at the moment that this _____ was fun for everyone *but* the young couple.

5 She glanced around the room, taking a _____ note of as many details as possible.

6 As the linen curtains swelled in the breeze, she noticed that the patio doors opened *out* on to the _____, rather than *in* to the room.

7 She eased a little gold pencil that the receptionist had given her out of her bag and added extra details to the hotel _____ she'd drawn that morning.

8 The receptionist – "Liza with a 'z'!" – had taken Zaiba and some of the other children round the _____ while their parents were busy unpacking.

9 She'd pointed out the twenty-six bedrooms, the library with its leather-bound books and the _____ hotel grounds and separate buildings.

10 Zaiba opened the phone's voice _____ again and put it to her lips.

11 "Bad – no *really* bad – _____ from the DJ booth close to the north-east window."

12 "Aunt Fouzia!" Zaiba _____, annoyed that she'd been discovered.

? FIVE Ws AND HOW

Answer the questions below. Look back at *Agent Zaiba Investigates: The Missing Diamonds* to find the correct answers.

1 What type of party was it?

_____

2 What were the three main ingredients for the party?

_____

3 What was at the top of the room?

_____

4 What colours were the bride-to-be's sari?

_____

5 How were Zaiba and Sam related?

_____

6 What was the name of the bride's fiancé?

_____

7 Where did the patio doors open out to?

_____

8 What had Zaiba drawn that morning?

_____

9 What was the name of the hotel receptionist?

_____

10 How many bedrooms did the hotel have?

_____

11 How did Zaiba describe the music from the DJ booth?

_____

12 Who found Zaiba under the table?

_____

◉ MULTIPLE CHOICE

Circle the correct answer to the following questions.

1 What colour was the bride-to-be's chair?

| black | silver | gold | white |

2 Who was Tanvir cornered by?

| eager uncles | eager aunties | eager cousins | eager siblings |

3 Where did the main entrance lead out to?

| the garden | the reception | the hall | the drive |

4 What did the receptionist give Zaiba?

| a map | a gold pen | a gold pencil | party food |

5 What were the parents doing while the receptionist showed the children round the hotel?

| dancing | talking | unpacking | tidying |

6 What were the books in the library bound with?

| card | silk | wood | leather |

7 Which window was the DJ booth located near?

| north-east | south-west | north-west | south-east |

8 Who is Fouzia?

| Zaiba's cousin | Zaiba's mum | Zaiba's aunt | the bride-to-be |

   Comprehension Ninja 7-8 © Andrew Jennings, 2021

👍👎 TRUE OR FALSE

Read the sentences. Put a tick in the correct box to show which sentences are true and which are false.

1 The party had food, music and films. True ☐ False ☐

2 The bride's hands were being decorated with henna. True ☐ False ☐

3 The bride was excited to have her hands decorated. True ☐ False ☐

4 Tanvir was the bride-to-be. True ☐ False ☐

5 The eager aunties were next to the punchbowl. True ☐ False ☐

6 Sam was Zaiba's favourite cousin. True ☐ False ☐

7 The silk curtains swelled in the breeze. True ☐ False ☐

8 The receptionist had given Zaiba a silver pencil. True ☐ False ☐

9 The receptionist's name was spelt with a 'z'. True ☐ False ☐

10 There were 26 libraries in the hotel. True ☐ False ☐

11 Zaiba wrote down her observations about the guests. True ☐ False ☐

12 There were at least 70 guests. True ☐ False ☐

13 Zaiba thought the music being played was great. True ☐ False ☐

14 Zaiba said that there had been no suspicious activity so far. True ☐ False ☐

15 Zaiba laughed when Aunt Fouzia discovered her. True ☐ False ☐

SUMMARISE

1 **Look at the first paragraph. Tick the statement which best summarises this paragraph.**

Zaiba was investigating a mystery at a wedding. ☐

Zaiba was at her cousin's wedding and was bored. ☐

The couple getting married were having the least amount of fun. ☐

Zaiba was discovered hiding under the table. ☐

2 **Look at the paragraph beginning 'Zaiba opened the phone's…'. Write one sentence to summarise what's happening in this paragraph.**

_____

_____

DRAW AND LABEL

Draw the statements in the boxes. Add your own labels to your drawings.

the bride's hand being decorated in henna	Aunt Fouzia finding Zaiba under the table

123 SEQUENCING

1 **Look at the sentence below. Write the numbers 1 to 4 to show the order the words occur in the sentence.**

As the bride-to-be, she sat on a gilded white lounge chair, wearing a sari in deep red, orange and yellow.

chair	sari	gilded	yellow

2 **Look at the section from 'Zaiba opened the phone's . . .' to '". . .No suspicious activity so far-'". Number the sentences from 1 to 5 to show the order they occur in the paragraph.**

"Observations: number of guests one, two, three, four, five… uhhhh, at least fifty people. . ."

Sofas and soft seating at ninety degrees to my right.

Most people are on the dance floor.

Zaiba opened the phone's voice recorder again and put it to her lips.

". . .No suspicious activity so far–"

3 **Look at *Agent Zaiba Investigates: The Missing Diamonds*. Number the sentences from 1 to 5 to show the order they occur in the whole text.**

Zaiba saw her cousin stifle a yawn as she continued to sit patiently while her hands were decorated with the henna.

The tablecloth whipped up and a hand reached for Zaiba, pulling her swiftly out from her observation point.

It seemed at the moment that this party was fun for everyone *but* the young couple.

Most people are on the dance floor.

Zaiba felt a stab of sadness.

👀 FIND AND COPY

These questions are about *Agent Zaiba Investigates: The Missing Diamonds*.

1 Look at the first paragraph. Find and copy a word that means lots of something.

_____

2 Look at the second paragraph. Find and copy a word that tells us that Zaiba loved her cousin.

_____

3 Look at the second paragraph. Find and copy a word that shows that Zaiba took a quick look around the room.

_____

4 Look at the second paragraph. Find and copy a word that tells us that Zaiba made a note of something without writing it down.

_____

5 Look at the paragraph beginning 'Zaiba opened the phone's…'. Find and copy a word that means the people who had been invited to the Mehndi party.

_____

6 Look at the paragraph beginning 'Zaiba opened the phone's…'. Find and copy a word that tells us that Zaiba is looking for people who are behaving badly.

_____

Comprehension Ninja 7-8 © Andrew Jennings, 2021

✎ CIRCLE A WORD

Read the paragraph below and then follow the instructions.

This party definitely had the three main ingredients for a successful Mehndi party in abundance – food, music and dancing! At the top of the room on a little stage was Sam. As the bride-to-be, she sat on a gilded white lounge chair, wearing a sari in deep red, orange and yellow. Zaiba saw her cousin stifle a yawn as she continued to sit patiently while her hands were decorated with the henna. Meanwhile her fiancé, Tanvir, had been cornered next to the punchbowl by some eager aunties who wanted to know *everything* about the upcoming wedding. It seemed at the moment that this party was fun for everyone *but* the young couple.

1 Circle a word that means the parts.

2 Circle a word that means a very large quantity.

3 Circle a word that means to prevent or stop.

4 Circle a word that means calmly.

5 Circle a word that means forced into a place.

6 Circle a word that means keen.

NOSE-PICKING NICHOLAS PICKERING

PETER BARRON

The following extract is the moment young Nick comes face to face with The Bogeyman after finding himself inside his own nose!

… It came round the corner, dripping with goo,
Disgusting and ugly, with a smell of beef stew.
With each step that it took came a terrible slurping,
It was snorting and grunting and farting and burping.

A good ten-feet tall and as wide as a bus,
It was covered in sores, all oozing with pus.
With one blood-red eye, half open, half closing,
Parts of its body seemed to be decomposing.

It had tusks like a walrus and a unicorn's horn,
The Bogeyman cometh, Nick wished he'd never been born.
For a while, he just sat there, frozen with fear,
"Mummy," he screamed, "I don't want to be here!"

It was all far too much for a boy to endure,
He started to run – so did his pursuer.
The monster was gaining with each giant stride,
Nick slipped on a stone, there was nowhere to hide.

The Bogeyman's shadow moved in for the kill,
His claws were like daggers – Nick's heart stood still.
After all he had been through, he was finally broken,
The beast opened its mouth… and was rather well-spoken:

"So, you're the young picker, how do you do?"
Nick was hit in the face with a globule of glue.
"Quite frankly, I can't think of anything ruder,
Than using your finger as a nasal intruder."

"And that means it's time to take your last breath,
You disgust me, my boy, time to pick you to death!"
Nick expected to die in horrible pain,
But then something happened he couldn't explain.

From the back of beyond, a wind gathered pace,
A whisper at first but then full in the face.
What started so gently, no more than a breeze,
Was now nothing to sniff at, a fully-fledged sneeze.

For a boy lost in his nose, what a very big issue,
The last thing he heard was a deafening ATISHOO!

(To be continued…)

The activities on these pages are about *Nose-picking Nicholas Pickering*.

✏ FILL IN THE GAP

Skim to find the correct area or verse of the poem. Then scan to locate the correct line. Fill in the gap with the missing word.

A good ten-feet tall and as wide as a bus,
It was covered in sores, all _____ with pus.

From the back of beyond, a wind gathered pace,
A _____ at first but then full in the face.

❓ FIVE Ws AND HOW

Answer the questions below.

What is the Bogeyman as wide as?

_____

What is the nasal intruder?

_____

◎ MULTIPLE CHOICE

Circle the correct answer to the following questions.

What are the Bogeyman's sores oozing with?

| juice | blood | pus | gunk |

What is Nick hit in the face with?

| a globule of glue | water | juice | a splash of milk |

🐾 TRUE OR FALSE

Read the sentences. Put a tick in the correct box to show which sentences are true and which are false.

The Bogeyman is eight-feet tall.   True ☐   False ☐

The Bogeyman has a unicorn's horn.   True ☐   False ☐

The Bogeyman chases Nick.   True ☐   False ☐

✏ SUMMARISE

Look at the verse beginning 'It was all far too much…'. Write one sentence to summarise what's happening in this verse.

_____

_____

🔢 SEQUENCING

Look at the lines below. Write the numbers 1 to 4 to show the order the words occur in the lines.

It had tusks like a walrus and a unicorn's horn,
The Bogeyman cometh, Nick wished he'd never been born.

born	tusks	cometh	unicorn's

🔍 FIND AND COPY

Read the lines below. Find and copy a word that means a noise so loud that you can't hear anything else.

For a boy lost in his nose, what a very big issue,
The last thing he heard was a deafening ATISHOO!

_____

◑ CIRCLE A WORD

Read the lines below. Circle a word that means rotting and decaying.

With one blood-red eye, half open, half closing,
Parts of its body seemed to be decomposing.

THE BLUE CROCODILE

ZUNI BLUE

Fay threw five pieces of meat into the water.

"That should keep the crocodile busy," she said. "Hopefully it'll eat the bait instead of us…"

The pair jumped into the dirty water and waded through as quickly as they could. Jafari kept glancing back, hoping the large crocodile wasn't close behind.

When they reached the slope, there was a rope hanging down it.

"Climb as fast as you can," Fay said. "Throw down bait if you need to."

"Throw down bait?"

"Yep," Fay said. "The big croc could be back soon…"

Fay grabbed the rope and pulled herself up. Slowly she slid her feet up the smooth slope, moving higher and higher. Twice she almost slipped, but she managed to hold on and keep climbing.

FICTION: EXTRACT

Jafari followed close behind her. He kept glancing back as they climbed, hoping the crocodile wasn't there.

Soon they were halfway up. Climbing got tougher near the top. The slope was much steeper, so their feet kept slipping.

Something tugged the rope from below. Jafari looked back and saw the crocodile chomping away.

"The croc is here!" Jafari cried.

"Keep climbing," Fay said. "I'll throw some bait down." She fished around in her rucksack. "Just a sec—"

The crocodile yanked the rope.

Fay slipped and fell onto her back. She slid down the slope, heading straight for Jafari. He tightened his grip seconds before she slammed into him. Together, they slid down, heading straight for the crocodile's open jaws…

The activities on these pages are about *The Blue Crocodile*.

✎ FILL IN THE GAP

Skim to find the correct area or section of the text. Then scan to locate the correct line. Fill in the gap with the missing word.

The pair jumped into the _____ water and waded through as quickly as they could.

He tightened his grip seconds before she _____ into him.

....

❓ FIVE Ws AND HOW

Answer the questions below.

How many pieces of meat does Fay throw into the water?

_____

Who grabs the rope and pulls herself up?

_____

....

◎ MULTIPLE CHOICE

Circle the correct answer to the following questions.

What is tugging the rope from below?

| a hippo | a fish | a crocodile | a shark |

What does Fay fish around in her rucksack for?

| rope | water | bait | knife |

....

↻ TRUE OR FALSE

Read the sentences. Put a tick in the correct box to show which sentences are true and which are false.

Fay climbs up a ladder to get out of the water.   True ☐   False ☐

Jafari keeps glancing behind him as they climb.   True ☐   False ☐

Jafari slips and crashes into Fay.   True ☐   False ☐

Comprehension Ninja 7-8 © Andrew Jennings, 2021

 SUMMARISE

Look at the section from the beginning of the text until '…wasn't close behind.'. Write one sentence to summarise what's happening in this section.

_____

_____

....

123 SEQUENCING

Look at the sentences below. Write the numbers 1 to 4 to show the order the words occur in the sentences.

Fay grabbed the rope and pulled herself up. Slowly she slid her feet up the smooth slope, moving higher and higher.

moving	grabbed	slid	slope

....

FIND AND COPY

Read the sentence below. Find and copy a word that tells us that they arrived at the slope.

When they reached the slope, there was a rope hanging down it.

_____

....

CIRCLE A WORD

Read the sentence below. Circle a word that means taking a quick look.

He kept glancing back as they climbed, hoping the crocodile wasn't there.

Quests in Epica © Adam Bushnell 2016. Reproduced with the permission of Caboodle Books Ltd
Comprehension Ninja 7-8 © Andrew Jennings, 2021

QUESTS IN EPICA

ADAM BUSHNELL

Emily sat up straighter and smarter than usual. She wanted to be let out for break time first. She had seen something stalk its way across the schoolyard earlier and she wanted to see if it was still there.

A cat.

Emily longed for a cat. Or a dog. Or a rabbit.

Or anything really. A stick insect would have done but she was not allowed pets of any sort in her flat where she lived with her mum.

The bell screeched madly and all eyes were on Mrs Hacking Bottom.

The smile that invaded her face was kept to a quivering line.

She loved this.

Power over children!

Emily kept her own gaze focused on her desk.

"Red group," the teacher said slowly, "You may go."

Emily and the rest of red group silently walked out of the classroom.

Once outside, Emily raced across the yard toward the patch of trees where the cat had disappeared earlier. She crouched low and peered behind the trees. Brown fur was curled in a ball.

Emily reached out her hand slowly.

Her fingers found fur. It was soft and warm. Emily smiled and sat cross-legged stroking the little creature.

It turned its head toward her and Emily gasped.

The cat was indeed a cat. But, it had the longest ears of any cat she

FICTION: EXTRACT

had ever seen before.

They flopped and lolloped over its eyes.

The cat-rabbit rubbed its head into Emily's hand and purred even louder.

It shook its tail with delight and Emily gasped again.

It had a huge bushy tail like a giant squirrel.

She also noticed that its paws were covered in green fur. *Green* fur.

What kind of cat was this?

It was half cat, half rabbit and half squirrel. No wait, that was too many halves. Miss Hacking Bottom would have been furious!

It was part cat, part rabbit, and part squirrel with green fur.

It was a . . . a . . . what was it?

A Squicabbit!

Yes, Emily smiled at the thought, a Squicabbit.

The creature padded toward Emily and curled up onto her lap.

It was pure bliss and pleasure.

A pet. A real pet. A pet that no one else had ever even seen before. And it was all hers!

Her smile broadened and then vanished as the bell for end of break boomed across the yard.

The activities on these pages are about *Quests in Epica*.

🧭 FILL IN THE GAP

Skim to find the correct area or section of the text. Then scan to locate the correct line. Fill in the gap with the missing word.

She had seen something stalk its way across the _____ earlier and she wanted to see if it was still there.

Once outside, Emily raced across the yard toward the patch of _____ where the cat had disappeared earlier.

....

❓ FIVE Ws AND HOW

Answer the questions below.

What animal is the creature's tail from?

_____

What does Emily call the creature?

_____

....

◎ MULTIPLE CHOICE

Circle the correct answer to the following questions.

What colour is the creature's paws?

| blue | brown | black | green |

Which of these animals is the Squicabbit not made up from?

| rabbit | cat | dog | squirrel |

....

🐾 TRUE OR FALSE

Read the sentences. Put a tick in the correct box to show which sentences are true and which are false.

The creature is made up of a cat, rabbit and squirrel.　　True ☐　False ☐

The Squicabbit winks at Emily.　　True ☐　False ☐

Emily takes the Squicabbit inside to show her classmates.　　True ☐　False ☐

 Comprehension Ninja 7-8 © Andrew Jennings, 2021

✪ SUMMARISE

Look at the section from 'It turned its head…' to 'Green fur'. Write one sentence to summarise what's happening in this section.

_____

_____

....

🔢 SEQUENCING

Look at the sentences below. Write the numbers 1 to 4 to show the order the words occur in the sentences.

It was half cat, half rabbit and half squirrel. No wait, that was too many halves. Miss Hacking Bottom would have been furious!

wait	rabbit	furious	squirrel

....

🔭 FIND AND COPY

Read the sentence below. Find and copy a word that tells us that the area of trees was small.

Once outside, Emily raced across the yard towards the patch of trees where the cat had disappeared earlier.

_____

....

◐ CIRCLE A WORD

Read the sentence below. Circle a word that means looked.

She crouched low and peered behind the trees.

MATHS HOMEWORK

ADAM BUSHNELL

Fayola was walking home from school with her friend Amelia. They were walking through a park, the same as they always did, then Amelia said,

"Can you believe how much homework we got for maths?"

Fayola sighed and nodded.

"I know. There goes our weekend."

"Yeah, but I've got a dance competition," Amelia complained. "When am I going to get a chance to do it?"

"Maybe in the car on the way there?" Fayola suggested.

"I feel sick in the car if I read or even look at my phone. Doing all of that maths is impossible."

"Late night then for you," Fayola said and put her arm round her friend. "Sorry BFF."

They walked a little further before Amelia said,

"Are you really my BFF?"

"Course," Fayola said with a smile. "Why?"

"Could you maybe do something for me then?" Amelia asked while biting her lip.

"Sure, what?"

"My maths?"

Amelia gave a strained smile. Fayola looked at her friend, then the floor, then back to her friend.

"I wouldn't ask," Amelia went on. "But it's the dance competition and you haven't got anything on this weekend."

"I might have," Fayola said. "Family stuff."

"Please," Amelia said in a high-pitched voice. "Pretty please! Pretty please with a cherry on top!"

Fayola sighed.

"I can't," she said at last. "We'll get into trouble."

"I'll pay you if you want," Amelia persisted. "How much?"

"It's not about money."

"Look, if you really are my BFF then you would. Come on Fayola, it's only once and it's only because of the dance competition."

"Miss will know," Fayola protested. "She knows my handwriting."

"It's maths," laughed Amelia. "She won't know."

Fayola sighed again. They were getting close to her house. If she could put Amelia off a little longer then she could just go inside. If Amelia messaged Fayola then she could be a bit stronger. It was easier to say no in a message than it was in person.

"Are you going to do it then?" Amelia went on.

Fayola bit her lip. She didn't know what to say.

The activities on these pages are about *Maths Homework.*

🖊 FILL IN THE GAP

Skim to find the correct area or section of the text. Then scan to locate the correct line. Fill in the gap with the missing word.

"I feel sick in the car if I read or even look at my _____."

"But it's the _____ competition and you haven't got anything on this weekend."

❓ FIVE Ws AND HOW

Answer the questions below.

Where are Fayola and Amelia coming home from?

_____

What is Amelia saying she won't have time to do?

_____

◎ MULTIPLE CHOICE

Circle the correct answer to the following questions.

Who might spot that Fayola has done Amelia's work?

| her mum | Amelia | their teacher | Fayola's tutor |

What does Fayola think would be recognised?

| her handwriting | her spelling | the paper | the lines |

🔄 TRUE OR FALSE

Read the sentences. Put a tick in the correct box to show which sentences are true and which are false.

Amelia wants to spend her time training for a football game.   True ☐   False ☐

Amelia feels sick if she looks at her phone in a car.   True ☐   False ☐

Amelia and Fayola are best friends.   True ☐   False ☐

Comprehension Ninja 7-8 © Andrew Jennings, 2021

⏱ SUMMARISE

Look at the section from 'Fayola sighed again.' to '...in person.'. Write one sentence to summarise what's happening in this section.

_____

_____

....

🔢 SEQUENCING

Look at the sentences below. Write the numbers 1 to 4 to show the order the words occur in the sentences.

Fayola sighed again. They were getting close to her house. If she could put Amelia off a little longer then she could just go inside.

inside	sighed	longer	Amelia

....

👀 FIND AND COPY

Read the sentences below. Find and copy a word that suggests that Amelia is nervous or worried.

Amelia gave a strained smile. Fayola looked at her friend, then the floor, then back to her friend.

_____

....

◐ CIRCLE A WORD

Read the sentences below. Circle a word that tells us that someone is speaking while annoyed or frustrated.

"Yeah, but I've got a dance competition," Amelia complained. "When am I going to get a chance to do it?"

THAT'S NOT RUBBISH

ADAM BUSHNELL

Khalid was walking home from school when he saw it. His friends had already run up the stairs to their flats. He was just turning the corner to his block when he noticed something moving in a skip. The skip was bright yellow with red letters on the side. The rubbish inside was piled high: rubble, soil, a rusty bike, bits of plastic and then something that wasn't rubbish.

Khalid walked up to the skip. It looked like a pillowcase only it moved. There was something inside. Khalid looked around. Maybe he should go home and ask his dad to come and take a look. Then the pillowcase made a sound. It was soft and quiet yet quite high pitched.

Khalid opened the pillowcase and yellow eyes peered back at him. He stepped back, letting the fabric fall from his hands. Then he opened it up again. The eyes stared out and a mewing could be heard. It was a kitten!

FICTION: CONTEMPORARY

Khalid opened the pillowcase wider with one hand. With his other hand, he reached inside and pulled the kitten free. Its fur was the colour of midnight. Its eyes were the colour of the sun.

He dropped the pillowcase and cradled the kitten in his arms. It nestled in to his warmth and purred loudly.

Who would put a kitten in a skip? Was it an accident? Was the owner looking for it?

One thing was certain; he couldn't leave it there. He'd ask his dad what he should do. Maybe he could even look after it, just until the owner came to collect it. He would put up posters around the estate so that the owner could find their missing pet. Khalid was thinking about how worried they must be.

Then he walked up the stairs to his flat. As he walked inside, he called, "Dad! Come and see what I found!"

The activities on these pages are about *That's Not Rubbish.*

✏ FILL IN THE GAP

Skim to find the correct area or section of the text. Then scan to locate the correct line. Fill in the gap with the missing word.

The rubbish inside was piled high: rubble, soil, a rusty bike, bits of
_____ and then something that wasn't rubbish.

He dropped the pillowcase and _____ the kitten in his arms.

....

❓ FIVE Ws AND HOW

Answer the questions below.

What does Khalid find inside the pillowcase?

_____

What does Khalid decide to do to find the kitten's owner?

_____

....

◎ MULTIPLE CHOICE

Circle the correct answer to the following questions.

What colour are the letters on the skip?

| red | green | white | blue |

Where is the pillowcase found?

| in the bin | in a house | in the skip | on the pavement |

....

🐑 TRUE OR FALSE

Read the sentences. Put a tick in the correct box to show which sentences are true and which are false.

The skip is filled with broken glass.　　True ☐　False ☐

Khalid finds a rusty bike and rides it home to show his dad.　　True ☐　False ☐

Khalid lives in a terraced house.　　True ☐　False ☐

Comprehension Ninja 7-8 © Andrew Jennings, 2021

⚡ SUMMARISE

Look at the paragraph beginning 'One thing was certain;...'. Write one sentence to summarise what's happening in this paragraph.

_____

_____

123 SEQUENCING

Look at the sentences below. Write the numbers 1 to 4 to show the order the words occur in the sentences.

He dropped the pillowcase and cradled the kitten in his arms. It nestled in to his warmth and purred loudly.

purred	dropped	nestled	kitten

👓 FIND AND COPY

Read the sentence below. Find and copy a word that tells us that Khalid held the kitten gently.

He dropped the pillowcase and cradled the kitten in his arms.

_____

🕐 CIRCLE A WORD

Read the sentence below. Circle a word that means broken bits of stone.

The rubbish inside was piled high: rubble, soil, a rusty bike, bits of plastic and then something that wasn't rubbish.

THE PRINCESS AND THE DRAGON

ADAM BUSHNELL

On a bright and beautiful morning, a king looked out of his castle window and decided to go for a ride on his horse.

"What a beautiful day," he exclaimed as he trotted over the green field and flower-filled meadows. Suddenly, there was a great rumbling sound that made the land shake. The horse neighed in terror.

A dragon appeared from below the ground. ROAR! It had curved, sharp horns and long, yellow teeth. Its green scales glistened in the morning sun. Suddenly, it belched a green gas from its mouth. BURP!

The king began to choke, the king began to gag and then the king fell down dead. Then with a rumbling sound, the dragon went back underground.

At that moment, the princess woke up. She too decided to go for a ride on her horse. But as she did, she saw the king dead on the floor. She cried and cried at first, but then became angry. She galloped back to the castle and rounded up all the knights she could find.

The princess then sent the knights to find the dragon. In no time, there was a great rumbling sound and the dragon appeared from below the ground. ROAR!

The knights galloped towards the dragon but it opened its mouth and BURP! The green gas filled the air and the knights began to choke, the knights began to gag and the knights fell down dead.

FICTION: ADVENTURE

The princess decided to get the help of a wise woman who lived in the hills. The princess galloped as fast as she could to the wise woman's house and knocked at the door.

"Hello," croaked the wise woman. "Can I help you?"

The princess explained the problem and the wise woman nodded. The wise woman took out a magic wand and said strange, magical words. With a flash and a bang, there was a helmet and a sword on the ground.

"This sword can cut through anything," announced the wise woman. "The helmet stops any poison."

"Thank you!" beamed the princess.

Wearing the helmet and carrying the sword, the princess galloped over the land until she heard a rumbling sound. ROAR! The dragon opened its mouth and BURP! The green gas was belched at the princess. With one swing of the sword, the dragon was dead.

The princess slipped down from the saddle and took off her helmet. The dragon might have been dead but so was the king and all of the knights. The princess began to cry.

Just then, the wise woman arrived and said more strange, magical words. With a flash and a bang, the king was alive again and so were the knights! The magic worked on the dragon too; it was alive. Not only was the dragon alive, but the magic had turned it into a good dragon who only breathed candyfloss.

The activities on these pages are about *The Princess and the Dragon*.

✏ FILL IN THE GAP

Skim to find the correct area or section of the text. Then scan to locate the correct line. Fill in the gap with the missing word.

In no time, there was a great rumbling sound and the _____ appeared from below the ground.

The green gas filled the air and the _____ began to choke, the knights began to gag and the knights fell down dead.

❓ FIVE Ws AND HOW

Answer the questions below.

What colour are the dragon's teeth?

_____

What chokes and gags the knights?

_____

◎ MULTIPLE CHOICE

Circle the correct answer to the following questions.

Who says the strange magical words?

| wise woman | wizard | knight | dragon |

What does the dragon breathe when it comes back to life?

| fire | water | candyfloss | butterflies |

🔄 TRUE OR FALSE

Read the sentences. Put a tick in the correct box to show which sentences are true and which are false.

The knights manage to slay the dragon.   True ☐ False ☐

The wise woman gives the princess a helmet and sword.   True ☐ False ☐

The king, knights and dragon come back to life.   True ☐ False ☐

🕐 SUMMARISE

Look at the paragraph beginning 'At that moment…'. Write one sentence to summarise what's happening in this paragraph.

_____

_____

123 SEQUENCING

Look at the sentence below. Write the numbers 1 to 4 to show the order the words occur in the sentence.

On a bright and beautiful morning, a king looked out of his castle window and decided to go for a ride on his horse.

bright	castle	ride	king

👀 FIND AND COPY

Read the sentence below. Find and copy a word that means that the king was struggling to breathe.

The king began to choke, the king began to gag and then the king fell down dead.

_____

🕐 CIRCLE A WORD

Read the sentences below. Circle a word that means to tremble or vibrate.

Suddenly, there was a great rumbling sound that made the land shake. The horse neighed in terror.

THE THREE BILLY GOATS GRUFF

ADAM BUSHNELL

Once upon a time there were three goat brothers. The youngest brother was small with a cute little beard. The middle brother was taller with thick brown fur all over his body. The eldest brother was huge and had enormous sharp horns.

The three brothers lived on a field next to a river. But the grass in their field was dry and patchy. On the other side of the river was a meadow with lush green grass.

"We should cross the river and live in that meadow!" said the eldest brother.

"We could use that bridge over there!" replied the middle brother.

"Oh no!" cried the youngest brother. "A troll lives under that bridge!"

"A troll?" cried the two elder brothers.

"Yes, a troll!" nodded the youngest brother. "He has a massive, curved nose and terrible, yellow eyes. His teeth are like daggers and his mouth is like a cave. He is always hungry and will eat us up!"

"Are you scared?" laughed the middle brother.

"Scared of a story?" the eldest brother giggled. "Trolls aren't real!"

"I'll show you that I'm not scared" shouted the youngest brother. "I'll show you that trolls are real too!"

With that, the youngest brother set off towards the bridge. He slowly trotted over the bridge when there was suddenly a loud

sound from below. It was a low and loud growling. Then, a huge face appeared at the side of the bridge. Yellow eyes glared at the youngest brother. A massive mouth opened and long teeth dripped saliva.

"Who's that trip-trapping over my bridge? I'll gobble you up!"

"You don't want to gobble me up!" called the youngest brother. "My brother is much bigger and tastier than me. Look, here he comes!"

The troll peered along the bridge and saw the middle brother getting closer. The youngest brother ran to the safety of the meadow.

The middle brother slowly trotted over the bridge when the troll bellowed, "Who's that trip-trapping over my bridge?" bellowed the troll, "I'll gobble you up!"

"You don't want to gobble me up either!" the middle brother cried. "My other brother is much bigger and tastier than me. Look, here he comes!"

The troll once again peered along the bridge and saw the eldest brother getting closer. The middle brother ran to the safety of the meadow too.

The eldest brother slowly trotted over the bridge when the troll bellowed,

"Who's that trip-trapping over my bridge? I'll gobble you up!"

The activities on these pages are about *The Three Billy Goats Gruff*.

🖊 FILL IN THE GAP

Skim to find the correct area or section of the text. Then scan to locate the correct line. Fill in the gap with the missing word.

"Yes, a troll!" nodded the _____ brother.

He slowly trotted over the _____ when there was suddenly a loud sound from below.

....

❓ FIVE Ws AND HOW

Answer the questions below.

Where do the three brothers live?

_____

Where does the troll live?

_____

....

◎ MULTIPLE CHOICE

Circle the correct answer to the following questions.

Which goat has enormous sharp horns?

| the youngest | the middle one | the eldest | none of them |

What colour were the troll's eyes?

| red | green | black | yellow |

....

✓ TRUE OR FALSE

Read the sentences. Put a tick in the correct box to show which sentences are true and which are false.

The goat brothers live under the bridge.　　　　True ☐　False ☐

The goats want to live in the meadow.　　　　True ☐　False ☐

The troll's teeth are shaped like daggers.　　　　True ☐　False ☐

 SUMMARISE

Look at the first paragraph. Write one sentence to summarise what's happening in this paragraph.

_____

_____

🔢 SEQUENCING

Look at the sentences below. Write the numbers 1 to 4 to show the order the words occur in the sentences.

With that, the youngest brother set off towards the bridge. He slowly trotted over the bridge when there was suddenly a loud sound from below.

below	youngest	bridge	suddenly

👓 FIND AND COPY

Read the sentences below. Find and copy a word that suggests that the grass doesn't cover all of the goats' field.

But the grass in their field was dry and patchy. On the other side of the river was meadow with lush green grass.

_____

✏️ CIRCLE A WORD

Read the sentences below. Circle a word that means bent.

"He has a massive curved nose and terrible, yellow eyes. His teeth are like daggers and his mouth is like a cave."

PUGLY SOLVES A CRIME

PAMELA BUTCHART

We watched as Glitterpuff tiptoed down the driveway.

She was wearing a long, dark coat with a hood that completely covered her head. But we knew it was her because we recognised her feet and her PAINTED TOENAILS.

We followed Glitterpuff for AGES. And we had to sometimes DIVE behind bins and trees because she kept stopping and looking behind her.

All of a sudden, Glitterpuff changed direction and darted straight into the dark park.

"Clem!" I hissed. "I can't go in there. It's COMPLETELY BLACK!"

Clem sighed. Then she grabbed my collar and pulled me into the park anyway.

It was HORRIBLE. I couldn't see a thing and the ground was wet and something felt yucky under my paws, like SLIME or CAT POO.

I kept really close to Clem because she can see much better in the dark than me. But then she stopped suddenly and I crashed into her and yelped with fright.

Then someone started laughing.

And I COMPLETELY FROZE.

Pugly Solves a Crime by Pamela Butchart. The Author has asserted her moral rights under the Copyright, Designs and Patent Act 1988 or its equivalent throughout the world, to be acknowledged as the author of this Title. Copyright © Pamela Butchart 2016. Reproduced with permission of Nosy Crow Ltd.
Comprehension Ninja 7-8 © Andrew Jennings, 2021

FICTION: EXTRACT

"Well, well. Fancy seeing you two here," said a voice.

"CLEM!" I yelled. "There are GHOSTS IN THIS PARK!"

And THAT'S when I looked up and saw two things shining in the nearest tree! GHOST EYES! And then LOADS of GHOST EYES appeared ALL AROUND US!

I heard Clem gulp. "Those aren't ghost eyes, Pugly."

As soon as Clem said that, the WAILING started and I realised that the shining eyes were CAT EYES and that it was CARLOS and his STRAY CAT GANG!

So we ran.

The activities on these pages are about *Pugly Solves a Crime*.

🖊 FILL IN THE GAP

Skim to find the correct area or section of the text. Then scan to locate the correct line. Fill in the gap with the missing word.

But then she stopped suddenly and I _____ into her and yelped with fright.

As soon as Clem said that, the WAILING started and I realised that the _____ eyes were CAT EYES and that it was CARLOS and his STRAY CAT GANG!

❓ FIVE Ws AND HOW

Answer the questions below.

Who does Pugly watch tiptoe down the driveway?

_____

What two things do Pugly and Clem have to dive behind in order to hide?

_____

◎ MULTIPLE CHOICE

Circle the correct answer to the following questions.

What can Clem do much better than Pugly?

read	see in the dark	run fast	paint nails

Who is the leader of the stray cat gang?

Pugly	Clem	Carlos	Glitterpuff

🔄 TRUE OR FALSE

Read the sentences. Put a tick in the correct box to show which sentences are true and which are false.

Pugly and Clem recognise Glitterpuff because of her coat. True ☐ False ☐

Pugly and Clem follow Glitterpuff. True ☐ False ☐

Pugly pulled Clem into the park by the collar. True ☐ False ☐

Comprehension Ninja 7-8 © Andrew Jennings, 2021

🕐 SUMMARISE

Look at the paragraph beginning 'And THAT'S when I…'. Write one sentence to summarise what's happening in this paragraph.

_____

_____

· ·

123 SEQUENCING

Look at the sentences below. Write the numbers 1 to 4 to show the order the words occur in the sentences.

I kept really close to Clem because she can see much better in the dark than me. But then she stopped suddenly and I crashed into her and yelped with fright.

close	fright	dark	crashed

· ·

🔍 FIND AND COPY

Read the sentence below. Find and copy a word that tells us that Glitterpuff did something unexpectedly and quickly.

All of a sudden, Glitterpuff changed direction and darted straight into the dark park.

_____

· ·

🌑 CIRCLE A WORD

Read the sentence below. Circle a word that means emitting or reflecting light.

As soon as Clem said that, the WAILING started and I realised that the shining eyes were CAT EYES and that it was CARLOS and his STRAY CAT GANG!

SMALLER ONES ARE BETTER

A.F. HARROLD

Never get a pet bigger than yourself.
Oversized animals are bad for your health.

Take a snake that could swallow you whole.
A great white shark won't fit a fishbowl.

You might try to keep a polar bear in the freezer,
but don't tell your mum, 'cause the news wouldn't please her.

A bottlenose dolphin hogs the bath.
A big butch hyena is good for a laugh,

but when it gets peckish, starts looking for lunch,
the last sound you'll hear is a mighty meaty munch.

And it's the same with a tiger, the same with a lion,
don't get a walrus, and don't think of trying

21

POETRY

to befriend a blue whale: they're bigger than buses,
and when the food bill arrives, then you'll see what a fuss is.

Don't get a pet bigger than a person,
smaller ones are better. You bet you'd start cursing

if you had to clear up all the mess that you find
fallen to the floor from an elephant's behind.

A rhinoceros might be a tough old trooper
but it tends to overwork the tired pooper scooper.

So, stick with a stick insect, stick with the cat,
befriend a little rabbit or a mouse or a rat

or a sensible dog or a gerbil or a parrot . . .
or smallest and safest . . . a crunchy tender carrot.

The activities on these pages are about *Smaller Ones Are Better*.

🖊 FILL IN THE GAP

Skim to find the correct area or verse of the poem. Then scan to locate the correct line. Fill in the gap with the missing word.

You might try to keep a polar bear in the _____,
but don't tell your mum, 'cause the news wouldn't please her.

to befriend a blue whale: they're bigger than buses,
and when the food bill _____, then you'll see what a fuss is.

❓ FIVE Ws AND HOW

Answer the questions below.

What are bad for your health?

_____

What might you try to keep in the freezer?

_____

◎ MULTIPLE CHOICE

Circle the correct answer to the following questions.

Who is a tough old trooper?

| a hippo | a rhinoceros | a giraffe | an elephant |

What is the smallest and safest pet option?

| a stick insect | a rat | a gerbil | a carrot |

🔄 TRUE OR FALSE

Read the sentences. Put a tick in the correct box to show which sentences are true and which are false.

A snake might swallow you whole.　　True ☐　False ☐

Dolphins hog the bath.　　True ☐　False ☐

Hyenas are good for a cry.　　True ☐　False ☐

Comprehension Ninja 7-8 © Andrew Jennings, 2021

✏ SUMMARISE

Look at the verse beginning 'to befriend a blue whale…'. Write one sentence to summarise what's happening in this verse.

_____

_____

....

🔢 SEQUENCING

Look at the lines below. Write the numbers 1 to 4 to show the order the words occur in the lines.

And it's the same with a tiger, the same with a lion,
don't get a walrus, and don't think of trying

lion	walrus	tiger	trying

....

👓 FIND AND COPY

Read the verse below. Find and copy a word that tells us that the scooper has too much to do.

A rhinoceros might be a tough old trooper
but it tends to overwork the tired pooper scooper.

_____

....

🔍 CIRCLE A WORD

Read the verse below. Circle a word that means to make friends with.

> to befriend a blue whale: they're bigger than buses,
> and when the food bill arrives, then you'll see what a fuss is.

ALIEN INVASION

CHRIS HOLE

The world is in shock today after a group of visitors arrived on our planet from outer space.

People from around the world reported seeing unusual circular shapes appearing in the sky last night. They described them as being covered in bright lights and moving quickly.

Later, it was revealed that these shapes were actually spaceships which have now landed on several places on Earth.

The first reported sighting was made by Joe Ford, a farmer in Texas, USA. He revealed how a huge, bright object had appeared in the sky and then landed in the middle of his field.

"I was terrified," the farmer said. "It lit up the whole sky and then I watched it come closer and closer to my farm. When I saw it had landed, I called the police because I wasn't sure what to do! The police arrived and put a cordon around the area. I'm not sure what is in there but I've never seen anything like it before!"

FICTIONAL NEWSPAPER ARTICLE

Following the first sighting, many other reports appeared online last night. Similar events were also reported in France, Italy and Dubai. Photographs of the ships show they are all a similar size and shape and covered in white lights. It is unclear what or who is actually on the ships.

Maria Diaz, head of the International Space Federation, said that the sightings finally confirm that Earth is not the only planet which is home to living things.

"Although we are yet to find out what is on these ships, it seems that we now know that aliens do actually exist and it seems that we will meet some very soon," she said.

"They seem to have come in peace and are not a danger to us or our planet."

Leaders of countries across the world have told people not to approach the spaceships themselves. Anybody who spots a spaceship should call the police straight away.

The activities on these pages are about *Alien Invasion*.

🖊 FILL IN THE GAP

Skim to find the correct area or section of the text. Then scan to locate the correct line. Fill in the gap with the missing word.

People from around the world reported seeing unusual _____ shapes appearing in the sky last night.

It is _____ what or who is actually on the ships.

....

❓ FIVE Ws AND HOW

Answer the questions below.

Where does Joe Ford live?

_____

Who does Maria Diaz work for?

_____

....

◎ MULTIPLE CHOICE

Circle the correct answer to the following questions.

Where were similar events reported?

| France | Argentina | Mexico | Montenegro |

If someone spots a spaceship, who should they contact?

| Maria Diaz | Joe Ford | International Space Federation | the police |

....

✪ TRUE OR FALSE

Read the sentences. Put a tick in the correct box to show which sentences are true and which are false.

The ships are covered in red lights.   True ☐   False ☐

Maria Diaz is a farmer in Texas.   True ☐   False ☐

World leaders have told people to approach and welcome the spaceships.   True ☐   False ☐

⏱ SUMMARISE

Look at the paragraph beginning 'The first reported sighting…'. Write one sentence to summarise what's happening in this paragraph.

_____

_____

....

🔢 SEQUENCING

Look at the sentence below. Write the numbers 1 to 4 to show the order the words occur in the sentence.

"Although we are yet to find out what is on these ships, it seems that we now know that aliens do actually exist and it seems that we will meet some very soon," she said.

soon	exist	ships	aliens

....

👓 FIND AND COPY

Read the sentence below. Find and copy a word that means multiple, or three or more.

Later, it was revealed that these shapes were actually spaceships which have now landed on several places on Earth.

_____

....

◐ CIRCLE A WORD

Read the sentence below. Circle a word that means not normal.

People from around the world reported seeing unusual circular shapes appearing in the sky last night.

Go and Get a Haircut by Andrew McWhirter from *I Bet I Can Make you Laugh: Poems by Joshua Seigal and Friends*, © Andrew McWhirter 2013. Reproduced with the permission of Bloomsbury Publishing Plc
Comprehension Ninja 7-8 © Andrew Jennings, 2021

GO AND GET A HAIRCUT

ANDREW McWHIRTER

Go and get a haircut,
It's looking rather long,
Go and ask the barber
He'll tell you I'm not wrong.
It's just that I prefer it
Not covering your face,
Go and get a haircut
And I'll be off your case.

Go and get a haircut.
Go and make it neat.
It's grown beyond your shoulders
It's grown beyond your feet.
You can measure it in metres
You can measure it in miles
Go and get a haircut,
Try out other styles.

Go and get a haircut!
It's getting out of hand!
It's spread across the county
It's spread across the land.
You're mentioned on the internet
You're mentioned on the news.
Go and get it cut,
I've got a chainsaw you can use!

Go and Get a Haircut by Andrew McWhirter from *I Bet I Can Make you Laugh: Poems by Joshua Seigal and Friends,*
© Andrew McWhirter 2013. Reproduced with the permission of Bloomsbury Publishing Plc
Comprehension Ninja 7-8 © Andrew Jennings, 2021

Go and get a haircut,
The army's mobilized!
Reports suggest there's many dead,
By that I'm not surprised!
The Prime Minister's requested,
That you have a little trim;
that you go and get a haircut
And I agree with him!

Go and get a haircut,
Evacuations have begun.
We're abandoning the planet
We're off to find another one.
I'm off to catch a spaceship
But in case you do decide
To go and get a haircut,
I've left a tenner on the side.

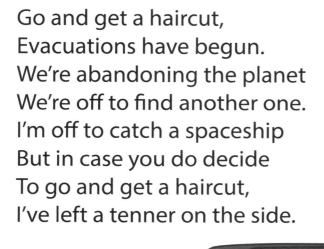

The activities on these pages are about *Go and Get A Haircut.*

🖋 FILL IN THE GAP

Skim to find the correct area or verse of the poem. Then scan to locate the correct line. Fill in the gap with the missing word.

Go and get it cut,
I've got a _____ you can use!

We're _____ the planet
We're off to find another one.

....

❓ FIVE Ws AND HOW

Answer the questions below.

What is everyone abandoning?

_____

How much money has been left on the side?

_____

....

◎ MULTIPLE CHOICE

Circle the correct answer to the following questions.

What is the reader told to try out during a haircut?

| hair dye | hair bobbles | hair pins | other styles |

What has been mobilized?

| hairdressers | the navy | the army | the police |

....

🦮 TRUE OR FALSE

Read the sentences. Put a tick in the correct box to show which sentences are true and which are false.

You can measure the hair in miles.   True ☐   False ☐

The hair has been mentioned on the news.   True ☐   False ☐

The Queen has requested the hair to be cut.   True ☐   False ☐

✏ SUMMARISE

Look at the last verse of the poem. Write one sentence to summarise what's happening in this verse.

_____

_____

....

123 SEQUENCING

Look at the lines below. Write the numbers 1 to 4 to show the order the words occur in the lines.

You're mentioned on the internet
You're mentioned on the news.
Go and get it cut,
I've got a chainsaw you can use!

cut	news	chainsaw	internet

....

👓 FIND AND COPY

Read the lines below. Find and copy a word that means to look tidy.

Go and get a haircut.
Go and make it neat.

_____

....

✎ CIRCLE A WORD

Read the lines below. Circle a word that means leaving a place with no plans to return.

Go and get a haircut,
Evacuations have begun.
We're abandoning the planet
We're off to find another one.

THE PATH OF FINN McCOOL

SALLY PRUE

If you go to Northern Ireland, and you catch the 172 bus to Ballycastle, then you'll get to one of the very strangest places in the world.

There by the sea you'll find the Giant's Causeway.

And you'll hardly be able to believe your eyes at the sight of it.

A great wide path of black stones, it is, all cut with straight sides to them, and fitting together as snug as a honeycomb.

And where does the path go? It goes straight out from the shore and down under the waves of the Irish Sea.

Now, you'll be wondering why anyone should build a path that doesn't go anywhere. But if you have a boat, and you feel like an adventure, you can sail across the sea to Staffa in Scotland – and there you'll find the other end of the path coming up out on to the land again.

And each stone is so heavy that there's never been any man alive strong enough to lift it.

FICTION: EXTRACT

Now, this is the story of how the path was made, and why most of the stones are under the sea. So that now you need a boat to get to Scotland.

It happened long ago, in the times when there were giants and Little Folk living in Ireland.

Now, the giants were good people. They were very handy if you wanted your house moved so you had a better view, or so you could put a river between you and your relations. In fact, the giants gave little trouble except for one terrible big, boasting fellow who was called Finn McCool.

Finn McCool was sixteen metres and two centimetres tall, and the Little Folk were always having to run for their lives when he came clumping along, not looking where he was going.

Now, this giant was lucky enough to have a wife and a baby. The baby was a sweet child, not much more than five metres long, and luckily taking after its mother. Finn's wife was called Oona, and the only silly thing she'd ever done in her life was to marry Finn McCool.

The activities on these pages are about *The Path of Finn McCool*.

✏️ FILL IN THE GAP

Skim to find the correct area or section of the text. Then scan to locate the correct line. Fill in the gap with the missing word.

If you go to Northern Ireland, and you catch the 172 bus to Ballycastle, then you'll get to one of the very _____ places in the world.

A great wide path of black stones, it is, all cut with straight sides to them, and fitting together as snug as a _____.

··

❓ FIVE Ws AND HOW

Answer the questions below.

What is the name of the causeway?

_____

Where does the path come up out on to the land again?

_____

··

◎ MULTIPLE CHOICE

Circle the correct answer to the following questions.

What does the text say you need to get to Staffa in Scotland?

| a car | a motorbike | a boat | an aeroplane |

How tall was Finn McCool?

| 16 metres, 2 cm | 60 metres, 12 cm | 16 metres, 12 cm | 18 metres, 2 cm |

··

🐷 TRUE OR FALSE

Read the sentences. Put a tick in the correct box to show which sentences are true and which are false.

No man has ever lifted a stone from the Giant's Causeway.   True ☐ False ☐

The 127 bus takes you to the Giant's Causeway.   True ☐ False ☐

Finn McCool's baby is four metres long.   True ☐ False ☐

Comprehension Ninja 7-8 © Andrew Jennings, 2021

✦ SUMMARISE

Look at the paragraph beginning 'Now, the giants...'. Write one sentence to summarise what's happening in this paragraph.

_____

_____

🔢 SEQUENCING

Look at the sentence below. Write the numbers 1 to 4 to show the order the words occur in the sentence.

But if you have a boat, and you feel like an adventure, you can sail across the sea to Staffa in Scotland – and there you'll find the other end of the path coming up out on to the land again.

land	boat	Staffa	adventure

👀 FIND AND COPY

Read the sentence below. Find and copy a word that tells us that Finn McCool always talked about how great he was.

In fact, the giants gave little trouble except for one terrible big, boasting fellow who was called Finn McCool.

_____

🔍 CIRCLE A WORD

Read the sentence below. Circle a word that means walking with heavy steps.

Finn McCool was sixteen metres and two centimetres tall, and the Little Folk were always having to run for their lives when he came clumping along, not looking where he was going.

1. AN UNUSUAL CAKE

FILL IN THE GAP

1. cupboard
2. flour
3. chocolate
4. 50
5. spoon
6. ingredients
7. courgette
8. greased
9. margarine
10. lovely
11. delicious

FIVE Ws AND HOW

1. Anya
2. self-raising
3. 50
4. 25
5. a mixer
6. 1 / an egg
7. 180°C
8. 20 minutes
9. a skewer
10. when the cake is cool
11. courgette
12. Dad

MULTIPLE CHOICE

1. cupboard
2. 1
3. 180°C
4. 20 to 25 minutes
5. margarine
6. 20
7. a skewer
8. courgette cake

TRUE OR FALSE

1. False
2. True
3. False
4. False
5. True
6. False
7. False
8. True
9. False
10. False
11. True
12. False
13. True
14. False
15. False

SUMMARISE

1. Anya started to help her dad find the ingredients.
2. Anya helps her dad to make a cake and is surprised that courgette is one of the ingredients.

SEQUENCING

1. 3 2 1 4
2. 3 4 1 2 5
3. 1 3 2 5 4

FIND AND COPY

1. nodded
2. measure
3. ingredients
4. greased
5. spooned
6. sliced

CIRCLE A WORD

1. noisy
2. fluffy
3. texture
4. powder
5. mix

2. MAUII AND THE SUN

FILL IN THE GAP

1. travel
2. sky
3. unhappy
4. ocean
5. Mauii
6. rope
7. coconuts
8. sun
9. plunged
10. plaited
11. ocean
12. thanks

FIVE Ws AND HOW

1. at top speed
2. unhappy
3. night time
4. to travel slowly across the sky
5. coconuts
6. a really long rope
7. the sun
8. pulled and sizzled / burned through the rope
9. Mauii's sister
10. her hair
11. cut all her hair off
12. to travel slowly across the sky

MULTIPLE CHOICE

1. a very long time ago
2. very, very long
3. travel slowly
4. coconuts
5. plaits them
6. the edge of the ocean
7. brother and sister
8. "No way!"

TRUE OR FALSE

1. True
2. True
3. False
4. False
5. False
6. True
7. True
8. True
9. True
10. False
11. False
12. False
13. True
14. False
15. True

SUMMARISE

1. Mauii caught the sun with the rope, but the sun burned through it.
2. Mauii asked his sister if he could cut off her hair to make magical rope and although she said no at first she then said yes.

SEQUENCING

1. 4 2 1 3
2. 4 5 2 1 3
3. 1 4 2 3 5

FIND AND COPY

1. Race
2. hero
3. caught
4. sizzled
5. beautiful
6. called

CIRCLE A WORD

1. angry
2. edge
3. ocean
4. racing
5. plunged

3. STONE AGE GIRL

FILL IN THE GAP

1. reed
2. waded
3. girl
4. pyramid
5. waterproof
6. smoothed
7. tents
8. berries
9. rabbit
10. lookout
11. dangerous
12. burned

FIVE Ws AND HOW

1. the river
2. a flint axe
3. ducks
4. reed
5. fishing
6. pyramid
7. animal hide
8. the duck that had been killed
9. the storyteller
10. in the distance
11. to gather berries
12. in a tall tree

MULTIPLE CHOICE

1. duck
2. a large fire
3. rabbit skin
4. in a tall tree
5. dogs
6. blackberries
7. a twig
8. boar

TRUE OR FALSE

1. False
2. True
3. True
4. True
5. False
6. True
7. True
8. True
9. False
10. False
11. False
12. True
13. True
14. True
15. False

SUMMARISE

1. The girl is picking berries in the woods.
2. The girl should be picking berries but she is looking at the lookout in the tall tree who is watching for dangerous animals coming out of the forest.

SEQUENCING

1. 4 2 1 3
2. 4 5 1 2 3
3. 4 3 5 1 2

FIND AND COPY

1. unaware
2. tough
3. pluck
4. enthralled
5. lack
6. snapped

CIRCLE A WORD

1. carve
2. hunters
3. storyteller
4. tales
5. enthralled

4. THE LOST TOMB

FILL IN THE GAP

1. pyramid
2. flaming
3. tumbling
4. hieroglyphs
5. foolhardily
6. repeating
7. bowing
8. axe
9. journey
10. shoulders
11. cobras
12. centre

FIVE Ws AND HOW

1. a temple guardian
2. a flaming torch
3. traps
4. tumbling into pits of lava or spikes
5. on walls / either side
6. Thoth
7. his foot
8. an axe
9. hands and knees
10. the walls
11. cobras / snakes
12. a flaming torch

MULTIPLE CHOICE

1. a temple guardian
2. a flaming torch
3. lava or spikes
4. Thoth
5. a man bowing low and an axe
6. cobras
7. lethal
8. the centre of the pyramid

TRUE OR FALSE

1. False
2. False
3. False
4. True
5. True
6. True
7. False
8. False
9. True
10. True
11. True
12. True
13. False
14. False
15. False

SUMMARISE

1. The floor crumbles and a hole appears in the path, but Amir avoids it.
2. A nest of cobras are tipped onto Amir, but he uses the flaming torch to make them go away.

SEQUENCING

1. 4 2 3 1
2. 3 1 2 4 5
3. 1 3 2 5 4

FIND AND COPY

1. traps
2. clues
3. stopped
4. narrow
5. thuds
6. gently

CIRCLE A WORD

1. coiled
2. strike
3. lethal
4. shrugged
5. retreated

5. THE TIME PORTAL

FILL IN THE GAP

1. shimmered
2. water
3. wires
4. portal
5. travel
6. deep
7. furrowed
8. portal's
9. hundred
10. plant
11. laboratory
12. adjustments

FIVE Ws AND HOW

1. water
2. five minutes
3. ten minutes
4. Jenkins
5. one hundred
6. green
7. dinosaur
8. sauropods
9. carnivore
10. the scientist
11. animal skins
12. one of the people

MULTIPLE CHOICE

1. flickered and flashed
2. five minutes
3. ten minutes
4. she is engulfed by fluid
5. long neck
6. sauropods
7. two seconds
8. spears

TRUE OR FALSE

1. False
2. True
3. True
4. False
5. False
6. False
7. True
8. True
9. False
10. False
11. True
12. False
13. False
14. False
15. False

SUMMARISE / DRAW AND LABEL

1. The scientist encounters a group of aggressive people.
2. The scientist is surprised to see a dinosaur.

SEQUENCING

1. 4 1 3 2
2. 3 4 2 5 1
3. 4 2 3 5 1

FIND AND COPY

1. constantly
2. short
3. engulfed
4. herd
5. carnivore
6. solid

CIRCLE A WORD

1. gasped
2. stomped
3. towered
4. impossibly
5. noisily

6. HOME FROM THE SEA

FILL IN THE GAP

1. creek
2. lobsters
3. fisherman
4. seaweed
5. boots
6. potatoes
7. Maltings
8. gate
9. remembered
10. shed
11. fade
12. tears

FIVE Ws AND HOW

1. Saturday morning
2. crabbing
3. the edge
4. no money and no food
5. the jetty
6. fishing-boats
7. Jack's father
8. seaweed, scruff and straw
9. crabbing-stick and pail
10. the sea-man / Jack's Dad
11. three gold coins
12. Jack's Dad / father

MULTIPLE CHOICE

1. crabbing
2. flotsam and jetsam
3. Mum
4. 'Morning!'
5. wavy
6. the garden shed
7. gold coins
8. fades away

TRUE OR FALSE

1. False
2. False
3. False
4. True
5. False
6. True
7. True
8. False
9. True
10. True
11. False
12. True
13. False
14. True
15. False

SUMMARISE / DRAW AND LABEL

1. Jack sees a man on the jetty where fishermen used to unload their catch.
2. Jack runs home but when he gets there the sea-man is waiting for him.

SEQUENCING

1. 2 3 4 1
2. 3 4 5 1 2
3. 2 1 4 5 3

FIND AND COPY

1. crabbing
2. unloaded
3. tangled
4. dared
5. remembered / recognized
6. strode

CIRCLE A WORD

1. starched
2. decorated
3. overcooked
4. pail
5. scarcely

7. LITTLE RED RIDING HOOD

FILL IN THE GAP

1. meal
2. knocked
3. leer
4. curled
5. smiled
6. caviare
7. forgot
8. matter
9. knickers
10. creature's
11. hood
12. WOLFSKIN

FIVE Ws AND HOW

1. a decent meal
2. Grandma's
3. she is terrified
4. one
5. Little Red Riding Hood
6. Grandma's clothes
7. in Grandma's chair
8. caviare
9. a lovely great big furry coat
10. a pistol
11. at Wolf's head / at the creature's head
12. a WOLFSKIN COAT

MULTIPLE CHOICE

1. his horrid grin
2. 'May I come in?'
3. one
4. the kitchen
5. Grandma's clothes
6. caviare
7. her knickers
8. his head

TRUE OR FALSE

1. False
2. False
3. True
4. False
5. False

6. False
7. False
8. True
9. False
10. False
11. False
12. False
13. False
14. True
15. True

SUMMARISE

1. Little Red Riding Hood shoots the wolf and turns him into a coat.
2. The wolf eats Grandma but is still hungry so decides to eat Little Red Riding Hood.

SEQUENCING

1. 4 2 1 3
2. 4 5 1 2 3
3. 4 2 3 5 1

FIND AND COPY

1. terrified
2. leer
3. flickers
4. whips
5. aims
6. WOLFSKIN

CIRCLE A WORD

1. decent
2. knocked
3. horrid
4. tough
5. wailed

8. THE GOLDEN LIONS

FILL IN THE GAP

1. love
2. slickest
3. determined
4. wearing
5. nimble
6. perform
7. steered
8. defensive
9. relentless
10. accuracy
11. cruel
12. rain

FIVE Ws AND HOW

1. siblings, mums and dads
2. Ezra
3. Ezra
4. Ellie
5. Ellie
6. Finley
7. Finley
8. Rima
9. Rima
10. Junior
11. Junior
12. Charlie

MULTIPLE CHOICE

1. astroturf
2. navy and gold
3. supporters
4. sweeper
5. Ellie
6. Rima
7. hunt and tackle
8. Charlie

TRUE OR FALSE

1. True
2. True
3. True
4. False
5. False
6. False
7. False
8. True
9. False
10. True
11. False
12. True
13. True
14. True
15. True

SUMMARISE

1. Finley is a defender who could also play as a goal scorer.
2. Junior loves to tackle and is a football manager's dream.

SEQUENCING

1. 4 1 3 2
2. 2 3 1 4 5
3. 2 1 4 3 5

FIND AND COPY

1. navy
2. dazzle
3. relocate
4. relentless
5. helpless
6. Roaring

CIRCLE A WORD

1. fame
2. unsurpassed
3. friendships
4. Training
5. worth

9. KNIGHTS AND BIKES

FILL IN THE GAP

1. wriggled
2. demon
3. fingerless
4. battered
5. Honkers
6. bunches
7. spray
8. toy
9. chin
10. caravan
11. arms
12. enemy

FIVE Ws AND HOW

1. a (large) duffel bag
2. a girl
3. two
4. Penfurzy
5. her (battered) sword
6. Captain Honkers / the goose
7. somewhere to sleep
8. red
9. a goose
10. a caravan
11. her arms
12. denim

MULTIPLE CHOICE

1. two
2. burglar
3. a sword
4. Penfurzy
5. Captain Honkers
6. frizzy red bunches
7. under one arm
8. goose pimples

TRUE OR FALSE

1. False
2. False
3. False
4. True
5. True
6. True
7. True
8. True
9. True
10. False
11. False
12. True
13. False
14. True
15. True

SUMMARISE

1. Demelza didn't want to send the stranger away into the terrible weather.
2. A creature is hiding underneath a blanket.

SEQUENCING

1. 2 1 3 4
2. 1 4 5 2 3
3. 5 2 1 4 3

FIND AND COPY

1. struggled
2. burglar
3. peck
4. whistled
5. icy
6. scared

CIRCLE A WORD

1. wriggled
2. rectangular
3. surrender
4. slouchy
5. burglar

10. GRANNY TING TING

FILL IN THE GAP

1. trumpeting
2. lime
3. caterpillars
4. wheel
5. bigger
6. waterfalls
7. cormorants
8. tadpoles
9. turtles
10. snow
11. Trinidad
12. admitted

FIVE Ws AND HOW

1. Shayla
2. deep, trumpeting
3. Michael
4. Granny's conch shell
5. (scary) caterpillars
6. Michael
7. London
8. ice-skating
9. to the beach
10. waterfalls / water
11. black cormorants
12. crabs

MULTIPLE CHOICE

1. lime
2. Granny's
3. a pod
4. weaver birds
5. tadpoles
6. crabs
7. turtles
8. cousins

TRUE OR FALSE

1. True
2. False
3. True
4. False
5. True
6. False
7. False
8. True
9. False
10. False
11. False
12. True
13. True
14. False
15. False

SUMMARISE

1. Shayla asks Michael if London is better than Trinidad, and he says Trinidad has some cool things.
2. Shayla hears a trumpeting noise outside and sees Michael in a tree blowing a conch shell.

SEQUENCING

1. 2 1 3 4
2. 5 3 1 2 4
3. 1 3 2 5 4

FIND AND COPY

1. spotted
2. scary
3. massive
4. wound
5. quiet
6. admitted

CIRCLE A WORD

1. trickled
2. clear
3. swooped
4. rummaged
5. collected

11. THE CHOCOLATE UNICORN

FILL IN THE GAP

1. sandcastle
2. Olive
3. walked
4. passed
5. edge
6. gloopy
7. knocked
8. wrinkly
9. chatting
10. Together
11. home
12. miss

FIVE Ws AND HOW

1. at a beach
2. a sandcastle
3. chocolate
4. on his t-shirt
5. in the sea
6. brave
7. her mum
8. Eric
9. a big wave
10. a sandy cave
11. his buckets and spades
12. Eric

MULTIPLE CHOICE

1. the rock pools
2. a bucket
3. his t-shirt
4. a moat
5. brave
6. the chocolate unicorn
7. her face
8. a cave

TRUE OR FALSE

1. True
2. False
3. False
4. True
5. False
6. False
7. True
8. False
9. True
10. False
11. True
12. False
13. True
14. False
15. True

SUMMARISE

1. Olive suggests that the chocolate unicorn goes with Eric.
2. Eric was too scared to go in the water and Olive understood how he felt.

SEQUENCING

1. 1 4 3 2
2. 2 3 4 5 1
3. 1 2 5 3 4

FIND AND COPY

1. love
2. together
3. screaming
4. again
5. shivering
6. chatting

CIRCLE A WORD

1. cave
2. buckets
3. shy
4. miss
5. forget

12. AGENT ZAIBA INVESTIGATES: THE MISSING DIAMONDS

FILL IN THE GAP

1. successful
2. bride
3. punchbowl
4. party
5. mental
6. garden
7. map
8. hotel
9. extensive
10. recorder
11. music
12. groaned

FIVE Ws AND HOW

1. a Mehndi party / a wedding
2. food, music and dancing
3. a little stage
4. deep red, orange and yellow
5. they were cousins
6. Tanvir
7. the garden
8. a hotel map
9. Liza
10. twenty-six
11. really bad
12. Aunt Fouzia

MULTIPLE CHOICE

1. white
2. eager aunties
3. the drive
4. a gold pencil
5. unpacking
6. leather
7. north-east
8. Zaiba's aunt

TRUE AND FALSE

1. False
2. True
3. False
4. False
5. True
6. True
7. False
8. False
9. True
10. False
11. False
12. False
13. False
14. True
15. False

SUMMARISE

1. The couple getting married were having the least amount of fun.
2. Zaiba recorded her observations about the guests and the music.

SEQUENCING

1. 2, 3, 1, 4
2. 2, 3, 4, 1, 5
3. 1, 5, 2, 4, 3

FIND AND COPY

1. abundance
2. favourite
3. glanced
4. mental
5. guests
6. suspicious

CIRCLE A WORD

1. ingredients
2. abundance
3. stifle
4. patiently
5. cornered
6. eager

13. NOSE-PICKING NICHOLAS PICKERING

FILL IN THE GAP

oozing
whisper

FIVE Ws AND HOW

a bus
finger

MULTIPLE CHOICE

pus
a globule of glue

TRUE OR FALSE

False
True
True

SUMMARISE

Nick tries to run away from The Bogeyman but there is nowhere to hide.

SEQUENCING

4 1 3 2

FIND AND COPY

deafening

CIRCLE A WORD

decomposing

14. THE BLUE CROCODILE

FILL IN THE GAP

dirty
slammed

FIVE Ws AND HOW

five
Fay

MULTIPLE CHOICE

a crocodile
bait

TRUE OR FALSE

False
True
False

SUMMARISE

Fay throws meat into the water as bait for the crocodile.

SEQUENCING

4 1 2 3

FIND AND COPY

reached

CIRCLE A WORD

glancing

15. QUESTS IN EPICA

FILL IN THE GAP

schoolyard
trees

FIVE Ws AND HOW

a squirrel
a Squicabbit

MULTIPLE CHOICE

green
dog

TRUE OR FALSE

True
False
False

SUMMARISE

Emily is shocked to see the animal is part cat, part rabbit and part squirrel.

SEQUENCING

3 1 4 2

FIND AND COPY

patch

CIRCLE A WORD

peered

16. MATHS HOMEWORK

FILL IN THE GAP

phone
dance

FIVE Ws AND HOW

school
her (maths) homework

MULTIPLE CHOICE

their teacher
her handwriting

TRUE OR FALSE

False
True
True

SUMMARISE

Fayola hopes to get home quickly so that she doesn't have to say yes to doing Amelia's homework.

SEQUENCING

4 1 3 2

FIND AND COPY

strained

CIRCLE A WORD

complained

17. THAT'S NOT RUBBISH

FILL IN THE GAP

plastic
cradled

FIVE Ws AND HOW

a kitten
put up posters around the estate

MULTIPLE CHOICE

red
in the skip

TRUE OR FALSE

False
False
False

SUMMARISE

Khalid knew that he couldn't leave the kitten in the skip.

SEQUENCING

4 1 3 2

FIND AND COPY

cradled

CIRCLE A WORD

rubble

18. THE PRINCESS AND THE DRAGON

FILL IN THE GAP

dragon
knights

FIVE Ws AND HOW

yellow
green gas

MULTIPLE CHOICE

wise woman
candyfloss

TRUE OR FALSE

False
True
True

SUMMARISE

The princess goes for a ride on her horse and is upset then angry when she sees the king on the floor.

SEQUENCING

1 3 4 2

FIND AND COPY

choke / gag

CIRCLE A WORD

shake

19. THE THREE BILLY GOATS GRUFF

FILL IN THE GAP

youngest
bridge

FIVE Ws AND HOW

on a field (next to a river)
under the bridge

MULTIPLE CHOICE

the eldest
yellow

TRUE OR FALSE

False
True
True

SUMMARISE

There were three goats who looked very different.

SEQUENCING

4 1 2 3

FIND AND COPY

patchy

CIRCLE A WORD

curved

20. PUGLY SOLVES A CRIME

FILL IN THE GAP

crashed
shining

FIVE Ws AND HOW

Glitterpuff
bins and trees

MULTIPLE CHOICE

see in the dark
Carlos

TRUE OR FALSE

False
True
False

SUMMARISE

Pugly sees lots of ghost eyes all around.

SEQUENCING

1 4 2 3

FIND AND COPY

sudden

CIRCLE A WORD

shining

21. SMALLER ONES ARE BETTER

FILL IN THE GAP

freezer
arrives

FIVE Ws AND HOW

oversized animals
a polar bear

MULTIPLE CHOICE

a rhinoceros
a carrot

TRUE OR FALSE

True
True
False

SUMMARISE

Being friends with a whale would cost a lot of money because they eat a lot of food.

SEQUENCING

2 3 1 4

FIND AND COPY

overwork

CIRCLE A WORD

befriend

22. ALIEN INVASION

FILL IN THE GAP

circular
unclear

FIVE Ws AND HOW

Texas, USA
International Space Federation

MULTIPLE CHOICE

France
the police

TRUE OR FALSE

False
False
False

SUMMARISE

Joe Ford from Texas, USA was the first person to report that he had seen the spaceships.

SEQUENCING

4 3 1 2

FIND AND COPY

several

CIRCLE A WORD

unusual

23. GO AND GET A HAIRCUT

FILL IN THE GAP

chainsaw
abandoning

FIVE Ws AND HOW

the planet
a tenner / ten pounds

MULTIPLE CHOICE

other styles
the army

TRUE OR FALSE

True
True
False

SUMMARISE

The poet has left ten pounds on the side for a haircut.

SEQUENCING

3 2 4 1

FIND AND COPY

neat

CIRCLE A WORD

abandoning

24. THE PATH OF FINN McCOOL

FILL IN THE GAP

strangest
honeycomb

FIVE Ws AND HOW

Giant's Causeway
Staffa / Scotland

MULTIPLE CHOICE

a boat
16 metres, 2 cm

TRUE OR FALSE

True
False
False

SUMMARISE

The giants were helpful, except for Finn McCool.

SEQUENCING

4 1 3 2

FIND AND COPY

boasting

CIRCLE A WORD

clumping

ACKNOWLEDGEMENTS

The authors and publisher gratefully acknowledge the permission granted to reproduce the copyright material in this book.

PAGES 58–59

Home from the Sea from *Short! A book of Very Short Stories* by Kevin Crossley-Holland © Kevin Crossley-Holland 1998. Reproduced with permission of Oxford Publishing Limited through PLSclear.

PAGES 68–69

Little Red Riding Hood from *Revolting Rhymes* by Roald Dahl. Published by Jonathan Cape Ltd and Penguin Books Ltd. © Roald Dahl Story Company Ltd, 1982.

PAGES 88–89

Knights and Bikes by Gabrielle Kent © Foam Sword Games 2018. Reproduced with the permission of Knights Of.

PAGES 98–99

Granny Ting Ting by Patrice Lawrence © Patrice Lawrence 2009. Reproduced with the permission of Bloomsbury Publishing Plc.

PAGES 108–109

The Chocolate Unicorn by Jenny McLachlan © Jenny McLachlan 2020. Reproduced with the permission of Bloomsbury Publishing Plc.

PAGES 118–119

Extract from *Agent Zaiba Investigates: The Missing Diamonds* by Annabelle Sami © Speckled Pen Limited 2020, reproduced by permission of Stripes Publishing Limited.

PAGES 128–129

Nose-picking Nicholas Pickering by Peter Barron © Peter Barron 2014. Reproduced with the permission of Peter Barron.

PAGES 132–133

The Blue Crocodile by Zuni Blue © Zuni Blue 2021. Reproduced with the permission of Zahra Brown.

PAGES 136–137

Quests in Epica by Adam Bushnell © Adam Bushnell 2016. Reproduced with the permission of Caboodle Books Ltd.

PAGES 156–157

Pugly Solves a Crime by Pamela Butchart. The Author has asserted her moral rights under the Copyright, Designs and Patent Act 1988 or its equivalent throughout the world, to be acknowledged as the author of this Title. Copyright © Pamela Butchart 2016. Reproduced with permission of Nosy Crow Ltd.

PAGES 160–161

Smaller Ones are Better from *The Book of Not Entirely Useful Advice* by A.F. Harold © A.F. Harold 2020. Reproduced with the permission of Bloomsbury Publishing Plc.

PAGES 164–165

Alien Invasion by Chris Hole © Chris Hole 2021. Reproduced with the permission of Chris Hole.

PAGES 168–169

Go and Get a Haircut by Andrew McWhirter from *I Bet I Can Make you Laugh: Poems by Joshua Seigal and Friends*, © Andrew McWhirter 2013. Reproduced with the permission of Bloomsbury Publishing Plc.

PAGES 172–173

The Path of Finn McCool by Sally Prue © Sally Prue 2020. Reproduced with the permission of Bloomsbury Publishing Plc.

Every effort has been made to trace copyright holders and to obtain their permission for the use of copyright material. The publisher apologises for any errors or omissions in the above list and would be grateful if notified of any corrections that should be incorporated in future reprints or editions of this book.